I'll Have the Fruit and Grains, Please!

by
Victoria Leith

Illustrations by
Charlotte Summer

George Ronald
Oxford

George Ronald, *Publisher*
www.grbooks.com

*A catalogue record for this book is available from the
British Library*

ISBN 0–85398–490–5

Printed in Great Britain by Biddles Ltd
www.biddles.co.uk

"What will be the food of the future?'

'Fruit and grains.
The time will come when meat will no longer be eaten.
Medical science is only in its infancy,
yet it has shown that our natural diet
is that which grows out of the ground.
The people will gradually develop up
to the condition of this natural food.'

'Abdu'l-Bahá[1]

Contents

To Fleur and Ramin Missaghian Shirazi
my dear friends,
who are shining examples to the world.
You are both in my thoughts and prayers.

Introduction

An exclusive interview with the author (by the author)

Who am I?

I am many things! A qualified teacher, a co-director of a performing arts company, a wife, musician and a writer. I am also a Bahá'í! I discovered the Bahá'í Faith when I was 12 years of age and decided to declare my belief officially when I was 16. For the best part of my upbringing I was the only Bahá'í in my family, although this has since changed. I enjoy acting and singing and living life to the full, which leads on to the next question . . .

Why do I want to write this book?

Well, for years I have taken an active interest in diets . . . many women do. I am also very interested in being healthy – to have health is a joyous gift! I suffered with a vast variety of skin ailments, colds and allergies while growing up and in the last few years I have been reading a lot on nutrition and different ways of eating which I have tried and tested and subsequently failed at miserably. A good friend of mine from university suffered physically and mentally from a form of severe arthritis. She experienced a whole range of therapies, which included taking a wide assortment of pills and steroids with ingredients I cannot even pronounce, let alone spell. The side effects of taking the steroids ranged from acute bloating and tremendous weight gain to feeling fatigued and depressed. This particular friend even had her legs broken as part of her medical treatment.

After visiting several specialists as well as a clairvoyant, who had her own theories as to why my friend suffered in so much pain, her doctor introduced her to a book which explained the theories and principles of the Hay Diet. This does not, as I initially thought, involve consuming vast amounts of dry grass but instead looks at an extremely simple approach to eating called 'food combining'. I was impressed, as I had heard of this method before. Another friend had followed this system and as a result had remedied her excess weight. Her partner, who originally suffered from arthritis, also followed the principles and all symptoms were completely alleviated. Both were full of so much energy, vigour and vitality that I was intrigued. I investigated and discovered that William Hay was not some newfangled nutritionist but someone who, spurred on by his own illnesses, devised this system nearly a hundred years ago, his main principle being, 'Don't eat foods that fight.'

My journey of investigation continued with the finding of yet another book, this time entitled *Fit for Life*, by Harvey and Marilyn Diamond, which explores new ways of eating, particularly how and when to eat the right combinations of food, again promising to eliminate a whole host of ailments and diseases.

Some years later I stumbled across some fascinating pieces of writing of a similar ilk that I was surprised I had not seen before. These writings were not compiled by scientists or lecturers in nutrition but by figures I deemed to be extremely important in my life at that time and still do to this day. They were the writings of

Bahá'u'lláh, 'Abdu'l-Bahá and Shoghi Effendi. Although I have since learned that there is no specific school of nutrition associated with the Bahá'í teachings, I was eager to learn more about what the Central Figures of the Cause had to say about this particular subject. I had read about chastity, backbiting and administration but never about food and health. Here was something that I could really get my teeth into! So, the main reason for writing this book? It is a natural progression for me – I have learned something new and would like to share the knowledge with others while continuing my personal investigation and development in the subject of health.

What is the fundamental aim of this book?

The aim of this book is *not* to give nutritional advice and pages laden with recipes (well, maybe a few!) but to look at what Bahá'u'lláh, 'Abdu'l-Bahá and Shoghi Effendi have written about food for the future and keeping a healthy body and mind. *I'll Have the Fruit and Grains, Please!* is not solely about food – it is about making inspired choices which will eventually lead us down the path to optimum health and well-being. Its aim is to be an inspiration for Bahá'ís everywhere and will hopefully encourage them to consider healthier ways of eating and living. I would like to illustrate the connections between our health and serving the Faith, thus abating any fears of looking after oneself, while also highlighting the importance of applying self-discipline and moderation to one's daily routine.

Another aim is to compile these writings in one small book. I have found over the years many passages relating to food, nutrition and general health but would enjoy having them bound together for easy access in the future.

Who is your target audience and how do you suggest they read this book?

The target audience is anyone who has an interest in this topic! I am, however, aiming it mainly at the younger generation – as they are considered to be the driving force of Bahá'í communities. The youth are in positions to challenge what already exists in our society and as they increase in strength and numbers, they will be the souls who will lead the way for our future.

As for reading the book . . . It is my hope that the pages won't just be read then filed away but used as a tool for personal development. There are quotations and writings in this compilation which will need careful study and possibly a dictionary to aid the reader with the scientific vocabulary. However, if people are struggling with it in some way, they should not think for one moment that this is not the book for them. They can ask a friend to deepen together and share the journey of investigation. They may find through discussion that they acquire more knowledge and perhaps get to know others on a deeper level. This book can be considered as a 'good conversation starter' and the most important parts, the writings of the Central Figures of the Bahá'í Faith, are there to be read and re-read for better understanding.

How long should the book be?

Not too lengthy. I would like it to be a short compilation of writings interspersed with activities and tiny essays of thought that would bring to people's attention what the Bahá'í writings say about diet and our health.

What approach to writing would you like to adopt?

My style of writing will take the structure of friendly conversation . . . as if we were in some form of discussion or workshop. I want it to be light-hearted and relatively easygoing, yet informative, providing a kick-start to the reader's personal investigation. I will include a few activities, which the reader can engage in to promote self-awareness and to inspire independent investigation of the truth.

What is your hope for Bahá'ís who read this book?

There is so much for us to learn as Bahá'ís and sometimes it can all become quite overwhelming. However, the more knowledge we acquire, the more deepened we become; our faith increases in strength, our abilities to teach are heightened by confidence in our newly-found knowledge. Therefore I would like to think that people will use this book to assist them in their personal lives and in teaching their friends. There are so many diets which harm rather than heal and these writings encourage simplicity and moderation in a way which is non-intrusive to the individual.

My hope is that more Bahá'ís will be supportive of their friends who are striving for a healthy lifestyle and that the ripple effect of writing this book will entice more people to investigate further living healthily and becoming 'shining examples unto all mankind, and true reminders of the virtues of God amidst men'.[2] After all, we only have one shot at living in this fleeting world of dust.

Taking Care of Number One

(Health Enables Us to Serve)

You should always bear in mind Bahá'u'lláh's counsel that we should take the utmost care of our health, surely not because it is an end in itself, but as a necessary means of serving His Cause.

Shoghi Effendi[1]

Question Time

Answer these questions either verbally or on paper before you read on. Give them at least five minutes' consideration. (On paper would be best as you can have a more visual interaction with your answers!)

1) Do you consider yourself to be a healthy human being? Explain your reasons.

Example:

'Yes, I am healthy as I eat an apple every day and walk up the stairs instead of getting the escalator in town.'

or

'No, I eat far too many pizzas from "The Hut" and exercise is putting fork to mouth and back down again.'

2) What does 'being healthy' mean to you? If health were a meal/a tree/a garden, what would it look like?

3) Do you think by making small or big adjustments to your daily diet and exercise routine you could improve your health? Would there be benefits in doing this?

4) Do you think you are being self-absorbed if you look after your health 'too much'?

Thank you! Now it is time to read on. There are no hard and fast answers to these questions – it is really a matter of how you feel within yourself.

I have worked with many children and adults who feel that they are being selfish for taking care of 'number one'. They tell me that they don't allow themselves to be healthy and creative because it takes up too much of their time. They don't feel as if there are enough hours in the day to look after others, let alone themselves. My husband and I had an in-depth conversation recently, exploring the realities, pros and cons of plastic surgery and whether or not it was an act of vanity for a human being to wilfully change parts of the body one was not happy with. Where would *you* draw the line between looking after yourself and becoming so obsessed with your body that the majority of your attention in this life was focused on your physical appearance?

This is an extreme, of course, and does not necessarily count as being a 'health' issue unless you are in need of surgical attention for medical reasons. People always have hang-ups about certain parts of their bodies but they usually learn to live with them and focus on the positive parts of their physicality. But what about feeling good from the inside out? From mere personal observation, I see people, especially youth, going on faddy diets with the sole intention to lose weight, yet there are more brands of chocolate bars and crisps on the market than ever before and soft drinks and snack machines are as commonplace in many schools as exercise books.

Current research shows that more people in the West are clinically obese and even though we are surrounded by the latest health crazes, kicks and diets, we are still a population of unhealthy people with stress levels high in abundance and no apparent time to sort ourselves out.

Here are some questions, which you will need to answer as honestly as possible. Do you overburden your body with masses of junk food then wonder why you actually feel like 'junk'? Do you 'super-size' your portions at fast food restaurants, feeling as if you are getting a good bargain? Do you complain of constant fatigue, suffer mercilessly from coughs and colds at the drop of a hat and spend days fighting off these illnesses only to be met by other offenders . . . perhaps more tiredness, a sore throat, even depression? Do you struggle through each day, looking forward to bedtime and dreading waking up the next morning? If you answered 'yes' to any of these questions, then it is time to face the facts! You are becoming a statistic – part of an unhealthy nation statistic and it time to make some changes for the greater good! Let's start the journey by defining 'food'.

The expression 'You are what you eat' perhaps has more validity than you would care to imagine. In that case, I am definitely an avocado with plenty of rye bread, wholemeal produce, vegetables, fruit and pulses. This, however, wasn't always the case – I used to be more of a 'two chocolate bars a day, snack on cakes and biscuits, seven mugs of tea with two sugars' type of person and this manifested itself in my physical appearance and, interestingly enough, my spiritual capacity. The connections between the two are manifold, which is why I personally felt compelled to investigate with one mission printed on the forefront of my brain – how could I improve my health? I still allow for the odd chocolate here and there and don't beat myself up for having a few biscuits but now I try to stick to the 90–10 rule – as long as my main diet is full of healthy foods, my health picks up and I feel better than when 90 per cent of my diet is full of sugar-laden, caffeine-loaded produce.

Just quickly jot down some of the major foods you consume on a daily basis. Keep these notes for later as you will need to analyse them further.

Up until a few years ago I was forever wondering how it was that I was so tired all the time. Why, I often asked myself, did I constantly have a cold/eczema/asthma? I did not know the answers and neither did any of the professionals I consulted. As well as having streams of unanswered questions, I would have never thought to connect my health, or my spirituality for that matter, to my diet but since my personal investigation began, I have discovered gems of wisdom that have enabled me to be free of all that I have just described and as a result I have been able to focus more on developing the spiritual side of my nature. Therefore, it is not just a 'good idea' but *imperative* to look after 'number one'.

Ask yourself these questions: When you are given the safety rules before taking off on a plane, who are you instructed to place the oxygen mask on first in the event of an emergency failure in the air supply? If you see somebody drowning, are you supposed to swim after them, potentially risking your own life, or throw in the life saving device to aid them instead? Can anyone sit in the emergency exit in a plane or do you have to be a person of good health? I once requested that I sit in the emergency exit row in order to have extra leg room on a very long flight. When I told the staff the reason for my request – I suffered from suspected osteoarthritis in both my knees and needed to stretch my legs out – they refused. They said they needed fit and healthy people to sit there so they could easily assist in an emergency.

So why do we feel that to take care of 'number one' is contrary to what Bahá'u'lláh wants for us in this life? You need to ask yourself the question, 'What is the purpose of my existence?' Bahá'u'lláh educates us gently through the short obligatory prayer that humankind has been created to know God and to worship Him. Yet how do you achieve a goal so immense during your time on this earth, which the Central Figures of the Bahá'í Faith assure is so fleeting? You can worship God through prayer, which takes place not only in the form of words but also in actions!

Let deeds, not words, be your adorning.

Bahá'u'lláh[2]

Let your acts be a guide unto all mankind, for the professions of most men, be they high or low, differ from their conduct. It is through your deeds that ye can distinguish yourselves from others.

Bahá'u'lláh[3]

We are exhorted to serve the Cause and to teach the masses but how is this truly achievable if body and mind are unhealthy? During my workshops on self-esteem and increasing confidence for younger students, which explore being servers of mankind, people always seem to hesitate when I ask what they are good at. Many of my students feel that to express vocally what their talents are is a form of egotism and they do not want to suffer the inevitable onrush of jealousy they expect to emanate from their peers. This is where a change of mind set is required. If you turn your thinking on its head and remind and educate yourself that talents are gifts from God, which in turn will enable you to serve your fellow humans, then perhaps you will feel more like shouting from the rooftops,

'I am a great singer! I inspire others with my music!'

or

'I am a very good listener! I volunteer five hours a week to visit schools and listen to children read.'

8

However, the less concerned you are with monitoring and improving your health, the more likely you are to shy away from utilizing your talents for the benefit of the human race. If you suffer continuously from everlasting illness, then you are inadvertently stopping yourself from being a teacher of the Cause which, consequently, will be a detriment to society and to yourself.

You may want to note at this point that Bahá'u'lláh does not forbid you to be unhealthy. It is not a law that we should be healthy beings at all times, and naturally, no one is perfect, but we are 'counselled' to take the 'utmost' care of ourselves.[4]

When was the last time you took the 'utmost care' of yourself?

I am the first to put my hand up and say that if I am involved in a project of some sort, I start early and work late and don't listen to my body when it has clearly had enough. My husband is usually the one who demands that I rest and do nothing for at least 24 hours in order to recuperate and, thank goodness for me, I listen to him. Because when I ignore the needs of my health, I always, without fail, become ill in some way. Then I spend time in bed lamenting that I cannot serve this precious Cause, which also needs daily attention. So it is in my best interests and the interests of people who still do not know about Bahá'u'lláh that I become fit and healthy as soon as possible. You may have days when you don't feel 100 per cent. You will have undoubtedly experienced times when you question your abilities and God-given talents, even your 'Bahá'í credentials'. However, 'Abdu'l-Bahá brings comfort with His words of wisdom:

> ... let each one of you be as a lamp shining forth with
> the light of the virtues of the world of humanity.[5]

You are allowed to shine! You are allowed to be healthy!
And there is no service in shrinking away from your talents because you feel as if you are 'blowing your own
trumpet'. We all have a trumpet to sound, so let's hear
them!

> Act in accordance with the counsels of the Lord:
> that is, rise up in such wise, and with such qualities,
> as to endow the body of this world with a living
> soul, and to bring this young child, humanity, to
> the stage of adulthood.
>
> 'Abdu'l-Bahá[6]

Get Well Soon

The mountain to better
health is exhausting!

It is now your duty as a Bahá'í, and specially as a young believer who has still great services to render the Faith, to make every effort to recover your health, and to be confident that by making such an effort you will be attracting the confirmations of Bahá'u'lláh, without which no true and lasting healing is possible.

Shoghi Effendi[1]

Question Time

Think back to a time when you were ill. You may have had a bad cold, felt lethargic or had a terrible cough. What action did you take to recover your health? (Maybe you took some sort of medication, went out for a walk, sought out a good professional . . .)

Did you just 'hope for the best', expect that the illness would soon go away, or did you care for your needs thus speeding up the recovery process? *How* did you care for your needs?

The quotation at the beginning of this chapter should bring you great comfort – you are *allowed* to recover and look after yourself. If 'number one' is not healthy and that means you, how can you be of use to anybody? If a parent is ill, the children and immediate family will receive reduced quality care and attention. If a teacher is off sick for a lengthy period of time, the students will need to work with supply teachers, thus possibly jeopardizing their education, as there is a danger of losing consistency.

I have a friend who has been ill for some time. He is aware that his health is suffering but he places the needs of other people before himself, thus prolonging his own illness. His recovery is slow and painful and as an indirect consequence others are suffering because of his inability to put himself first. He is being selfless – wanting to put the needs of others before himself – but in the long term, it is a false economy!

If you suffer from illness as a human being, you will not be able to reach your full potential. It is as simple as that and a fact that is very easy to sweep under the carpet. This is not to say that all people who are ill are not able to teach the Cause. I know people with life-endangering illnesses who are severely incapacitated yet are still wonderful examples to communities, joyously opening up their homes and serving the Faith to their fullest potential. I am talking about being unhealthy when you could quite easily remedy or, better still, pre-empt the impending malady. Some things will be out of your hands and become tests to your spiritual nature; other areas of your life can be changed and bettered through your own efforts.

> All that which ye potentially possess can, however, be manifested only as a result of your own volition. Your own acts testify to this truth.
>
> *Bahá'u'lláh*[2]

Let me give you an example. A wonderful friend of mine spent a day at a barbeque. She was already health conscious and had decided that even though she was eating out, she would still watch what she ate. She had lots of salad, vegetables and a vegetable burger. She then sat out in the glorious sunshine with her friends, chatting and socializing, not realizing that later on that evening she would be extremely ill. You may wonder why she was going to suffer so much when she seemed to be having a good day with lots of healthy choices.

The answer is dehydration. This particular friend did not drink anything at all for about four hours, which coincided with her sitting in the sweltering heat. Later in the afternoon, everyone played football in a nearby park, including my friend, who suddenly felt very peculiar. She had to rush home in a state of dizziness and was very ill for two whole days, experiencing headaches and severe stomach cramps. It took three more days to recover and all she needed to have done was ensure that she drank enough water and not stay out in the sun too long.

Prevention is better than cure!

I will now let you into a little secret . . . that 'wonderful friend' was none other than myself! It sounds better if I speak about the incident in the third person because I felt so silly. But why had I had treated myself in such a neglectful manner? I obviously hadn't done it on purpose – nobody volunteers to be ill. It is very simple. On that particular sunny day I just wasn't considering myself with due care and attention. I paid little notice to what was necessary for my survival at a critical point. Had I thought about it in advance, I would have known what the consequences could have been and prevented the illness. However, instead of beating myself up too much about it, I decided to allow for human error and convert this into a learning experience. I considered it as a 'social experiment', becoming a guinea pig for my own research.

The very next weekend there was another barbeque to attend. I sat in the shade for most of the day, drank plenty of liquids and the result of this forward planning was that I went home naturally tired and happy – I had been in excellent company and had eaten good, healthy food – the hosts had provided the guests with equal choices for vegetarians and meat-eaters. Most importantly, I had looked after *myself*, which enabled me to be fit and well the next day.

Illnesses can very often be easily avoided but you do need to remember that you also exist in the equation of looking after people's needs. There is no need to feel that you are being selfish in doing this – there is nothing 'self-absorbed' in ensuring you are well. I missed out on several teaching opportunities as a result of the 'dehydration incident' because I was bed-bound: I was not able to answer the door to a friend who needed to talk and had to miss out on a band practice. Both were potential teaching and creative opportunities that I was not able to take. What a huge ripple effect just for not drinking some water!

Therefore, to recap:

Looking after ourselves = better health

Better health = a clearer mind
A clearer mind = increased ability to focus, serve
and be creative

It is often a good idea to write things down to make clear sense of them. For instance, why don't you make your own chart to show how beneficial it is to be a healthy human being? Every time you think about neglecting your own health needs, you can be reminded how important it is to recover or, even better, prevent the illness in the first place! Look at what the possible consequences could be and then you may be inspired to think more about yourself, which in turn will help you to be of more service to others.

'But what if I do get ill?', you may ask. Invariably, even the healthiest of people will suffer at some point from illness. As already mentioned, the more illnesses you can prevent, the better but it is easy to have an 'off day'. We will look at how to implement changes of diet into your lifestyle for better health in later chapters but a good starting point for now is that you can ask for help.

Generally, we are not very good at asking for assistance. In Britain, where I live, it's almost taboo! I have friends who have been ill for weeks on end and then one day, after not having seen them for far too long, I learn that they have been in bed, suffering with a cold that just won't quit or a nasty sore throat and cough which leaves them feeling weak and unable to do anything for themselves.

In the Bahá'í writings we are asked to help others –

especially the sick and ones who need healing. By visiting the sick, you can bring happiness into their lives and will speed their recovery. 'Abdu'l-Bahá says that,

> We should all visit the sick. When they are in sorrow and suffering, it is a real help and benefit to have a friend come. Happiness is a great healer to those who are ill. In the East it is the custom to call upon the patient often and meet him individually. The people in the East show the utmost kindness and compassion to the sick and suffering. This has greater effect than the remedy itself. You must always have this thought of love and affection when you visit the ailing and afflicted.
>
> *'Abdu'l-Bahá*[3]

When 'Abdu'l-Bahá says this He doesn't mean 'everyone but you' – He means that all sick people should be visited. Sometimes people won't know that you are feeling unwell, so it might take a phone call from you to ask for that bit of much-needed assistance. If you have children, you might request an hour of somebody's time so that you can have a long hot bath, a nap or some time just to be on your own.

If you don't have any dependants and it's just you to care for, then a friend can be there for you IF YOU LET HIM OR HER KNOW YOU ARE UNWELL! If, for example, you are a student and unwell, and perhaps it's your first time away from home, tell your tutor that you have been ill and therefore will need an extension on an essay. You don't need to ask, you need to say it . . . without being reticent! Neglecting yourself in any health situation will only lengthen the time you need to recover and recuperate.

> . . . you should not neglect your health, but consider it the means which enables you to serve. It – the body – is like a horse which carries the personality and spirit, and as such should be well cared for so it can do its work! You should certainly safeguard your nerves, and force yourself to take time, and not only for prayer and meditation, but for real rest and relaxation.
>
> *Shoghi Effendi*[4]

When I was a teenager at school, when my friends were ill or feeling run-down, I would 'prescribe' them 'remedies'. They were a bit of fun. I would write a list of things to do that my friends had to follow as soon as they got home. A typical 'remedy' would look like this:

1) Go home and have a bath or shower.

2) Get into comfy pyjamas.

3) Make a nice warm drink and curl up with a book or relax in front of the television.

4) Go to bed early.

The list would continue and it would always bring a smile to the friend's face. It is often simply the mere thought that someone cares about you that is enough for a speedy recovery. They say that laughter is a good cure for anything and this is quite true! A happy friend who is willing to spend some time with you when you need picking up will aid you to get better. It is all part of the recovery process. If you don't believe me, try it!

> Know that nothing will benefit thee in this life save supplication and invocation unto God, service in His vineyard, and, with a heart full of love, be in constant servitude unto Him.
>
> *'Abdu'l-Bahá*[5]

3

When is There Time Even to Sleep?

Go back to bed, Vicky

. . . there are very few people who can get along without eight hours sleep. If you are not one of those, you should protect your health by sleeping enough. The Guardian himself finds that it impairs his working capacity if he does not try and get a minimum of seven or eight hours.

Shoghi Effendi[1]

Which sentence most applies to you?

1) I go to bed at a reasonable hour but my sleep pattern is often interrupted.

2) I go to bed late as there are no hours in the day to nurture myself so I feel like I have to cram a good few hours in when the working day is over/kids are asleep. I then need to wake up early in order to continue working/caring for my family.

3) I go to bed early and wake up early feeling refreshed and ready to start my day.

4) An actual sleep routine is not an option as I have too many essays and deadlines to keep plus lots of socializing to do.

No matter at what juncture you are in your life at the moment, you will need to consider sleeping. The quality of your sleep will partly shape how you function on a daily basis. Surprisingly, however, many people will happily compromise their sleep patterns even though they are aware of the consequences, as long as they are able to obtain extra time with friends, family, going out until late and being creative – I have many artistic friends who will happily work through the night to satisfy their creative thirsts but realistically they still have to get up early and some of them can get quite grumpy!

Others will have less choice. For example, your living situation can make a big difference to the quality of your sleep. I stayed in France a few years ago and the refuse collectors came every morning – at TWO! – to round up the bins. There was a lot of whistling, singing and scraping sounds, all of which made it impossible to get any real shut-eye. Then, at about six – in the morning – the streets were cleaned with the noisiest machines known to man! By this time, there was no point sleeping (or trying to anyway) so I would end up wandering around aimlessly in the daytime very tired and lethargic.

Another time, I was in charge of a dormitory of 26 girls whilst working in Camp America. Many would wake up in the middle of the night for various reasons, including being homesick and needing to use the bathroom. If I was on duty, I personally had to see to them. Nowadays, I live in a reasonably quiet street and I can usually sleep the whole night through with no external noises to interrupt me. We do have a garage repair shop next door as well as a man who sometimes shouts out of his window all night long . . . so I get to have a restful sleep nine nights out of ten.

However, parents with babies, toddlers or even teenagers will have to be prepared to be woken from once to several times a night. And if you are a student at college or university – you will have to make allowances for loud youth running up and down the corridors, scaling the walls and singing, right outside your room, pretty much every night!

You may wonder why I am discussing sleep patterns when this book promises to look at food and health. Well, I believe that all these areas are intricately connected. All are necessary for optimum well-being and it is a vital ingredient of good health to sleep well. If you do not sleep in a way that suits you, this can have a knock-on effect on your diet, which then affects your health. Then, of course, the consequences become more powerful and severe, with the result that you are miserable, tired, stressed and depressed – and after all that, how can you be of use to anyone?

Bahá'u'lláh encourages us to:

Deal ye one with another with the utmost love and harmony, with friendliness and fellowship.[2]

It is impossible to achieve this goal if we are sleep-deprived.

Think about a time recently when you said something to a friend or family member that hurt their feelings. You may have involuntarily snapped at someone or said a few too many harsh words in the heat of the moment.

Did you sit down and ask yourself the *cause* of your behaviour? Bahá'u'lláh says, 'Search for the causes of diseases.'[3] In my personal experience, I have found, generally, that people who are irritable and irrational will, at the root of it all, be suffering from sleep deprivation. I am sure that you wouldn't behave in an abrupt manner because you are happily motivated to do so. You don't go round snapping at your friends and family because you enjoy it. And you don't tend to argue because it is the highlight of your day. The most common cause of the reactive mind is tiredness and the state of your diet. Sleep deprivation will magnify everyday problems, making molehills into huge towering mountains. Little things that wouldn't normally bother you could send you into a flying rage if you continually miss out on a good night's sleep.

You may think that you are sleeping well enough but if you find that you are snapping at the littlest thing in the daytime or are falling asleep at inappropriate times, you may need to consider the following:

1) The time you go to bed.

2) The time you wake up.

3) How you wake up (or are woken up).

4) What you eat or drink before bedtime or even a few hours before.

5) Your diet in general – do you drink a lot of caffeine, for example, or eat a lot of sugar-based foods?

6) Your sleeping conditions – what else is in your bed-room? Does it also serve as an office?

7) How many times you get up in the night and for what reasons.

8) Your general stress levels – are things bothering you more than usual? Do you have unfinished projects on your mind that keep you alert and wakeful?

9) Are there issues in life that you haven't dealt with? When it is time for bed – perhaps the only time you've had to think quietly all day – is your mind racing away, dealing with those issues?

Unfortunately, we live in hectic times with deadlines, pressures and junk food diets, all of which contribute to ill health. You need to find some time to identify the problems you face and see how they can be fixed.

Every Problem has a Solution

It is up to you to find the answer. If you are not able to do this on your own, then perhaps you could ask a close friend or relative to consult with you and see if they can offer some impartial advice.

If you feel guilty (as I know some people do) for catching up on your sleep, see it as another way to be an efficient servant of Bahá'u'lláh.

It should be to such a degree that if he sleep, it should not be for pleasure, but to rest the body in order to do better, to speak better, to explain more beautifully, to serve the servants of God and to prove the truths.

'Abdu'l-Bahá[4]

I once met a great man who was very active and seemed to have unusual reserves of energy – unusual because he only slept for about three or four hours every night. However, he would also fall asleep during meetings, meals and sometimes even when talking on a one to one basis. It was quite endearing but also potentially danger-ous – what if he fell asleep when driving? If you cause a terrible accident because you are sleep-deprived, then of course, your chances of serving in this world are consid-erably lessened!

Another friend was finding it very difficult to jug-gle university life, a job she needed to earn money for her rent, and time to eat and sleep properly. One day, after months of poor eating habits and erratic sleep pat-terns, she went to her part-time job, which was cleaning wards and doctors' quarters in a hospital. She sat down for an intentional couple of minutes, which then became a two-hour, much-needed nap. She slept through her entire cleaning shift. Another time she went into work and was so tired that she accidentally dropped a whole trolley load of equipment, some of which was breakable and expensive. It was at this critical moment that she realized some life assessment was in order. It is not good to be harming yourself through neglect – it is even worse when you affect others.

If your routine or lifestyle at present does not allow you to get the recommended seven to eight hours of sleep, then it is pen and paper time. Write down all the possible obstacles that prevent you from acquiring the right amount of sleep.

Obstacles

- I drink a lot of caffeine in the evening.

- My children don't go to bed until late and they get up early.

- I have too much work to do and need to work late in order to get it all finished.

- I leave things to the last minute so I need to work through the nights.

- I drink water in the middle of the night, which wakes me up later – to go to the bathroom!

- It is too hot/cold in my bedroom.

- It's too bright in the mornings.

- I find it hard to switch off at night so lie awake for hours.

All of these obstacles have solutions but you will have to make changes and adjustments, do some forward planning and, again, maybe ask for that much-needed help you feel unable to ask for.

Here are feasible solutions to these obstacles:

- Try to cut caffeine out of your diet – if you must drink it, then refrain from having it after two in the afternoon.

- If you have children, get them used to a regular routine of bedtime. Younger children need more sleep than adults so, ideally, they should be going to bed much earlier. At first this might be a tough problem to tackle but with firm yet loving instructions and clear guidelines, eventually the problem should be solved. Try not to have a stimulating activity before bedtime which will leave their minds active and alert – a warm bath, a bedtime story, prayers and a cuddle will leave them feeling sleepier than if they watch a few hours of television, eat junk food as an evening 'treat' and go to bed on their own with no comforting interaction (the story and the cuddles!).

- Give yourself 'me time' – not only in the final hours of the day but also at times when you can be relaxed, uninterrupted and really achieve your personal goals. If you only leave yourself time in the last moments of each day, then perhaps you are not considering your own needs as much as you could.

Placing yourself first sometimes can be of benefit to many people, especially if it makes you a calmer and happier person.

- Plan your life! I used to swear by working at the last minute as the adrenaline gave me the pressure I needed to get things done. But I was only able to do this because there was no one else depending on me. I did get caught out from time to time when I forgot to do things because I tended to put smaller jobs off. The result was I let myself and other people down. I have a notebook now and in it I write daily my list of 'things to do', project ideas and anything else that requires consideration. I consult it every day and cross off items when they have been realized. It works – if used methodically and consistently – and as a result I am much clearer about personal deadlines and more inclined to achieve my goals.

- In the Tablet to a Physician, Bahá'u'lláh counsels us, 'Do not drink after you have retired to sleep'.[5] There are good reasons for this! Needing the bathroom several times a night will break your sleep pattern greatly and I am sure there is more wisdom in this guidance.

- I recommend leaving a window slightly open when you are sleeping. No matter what time of year it is, I always have the window open! This allows fresh air to circulate through and the stuffy air to leave.

If you are too cold, however, then this will also affect your sleep pattern. Ensure that you are warm and cosy but not so warm that you are uncomfortable. If it helps, place a wall thermometer in your room to monitor the temperature.

- If it is too bright in your room early in the morning then consider investing in some heavy curtains which will allow you to wake up at a more respectable time. Some people enjoy waking up to bright sunshine but for others – especially in the summer when it can become bright at four or five in the morning – it is a case of 'too much too early'. Alternatively, you could line the curtains you already have with some dark material.

- If you find yourself staring up at the dark each night rather than drifting off into a peaceful sleep, consider listening to some gentle music or natural sounds such as ocean waves, soft flowing breezes or light rain. You can obtain these sleep instigators in most leading CD shops and health stores. Great to put on a birthday wish list! I go to bed every night listening to the sounds of the ocean and it really helps me to switch off and visualize calm, tranquil scenes, which then induce sleep ZZZZzzzzz . . .

These are just some solutions to possible problems and as I am sure that everyone has their different obstacles in life, it will help you to write them all down, identify what you can and can't change and then ACTION THOSE SOLUTIONS!

> Strive to be shining examples unto all mankind, and true reminders of the virtues of God amidst men.
>
> *Baháʼuʼlláh*[6]

4

Health in the Form of Simplicity

H_2O – simple health

It is certainly the case that sins are a potent cause
of physical ailments. If humankind were free from
the defilements of sin and waywardness, and
lived according to a natural, inborn equilibrium,
without following wherever their passions led, it is
undeniable that diseases would no longer take the
ascendant, nor diversify with such intensity.

'Abdu'l-Bahá[1]

Mini Activity

List three positive 'cause and effect' scenarios in which
you take action and there is a direct result.

Example:
   I tidy and organise my desk (cause).
   My head feels clearer and I am more productive/
      creative (effect).

Now list three negative scenarios.

Example:
   I eat a huge meal (cause).
   I feel bloated afterwards (effect).

It is little wonder that we end up going wherever our
passions lead us. We live in quite a wayward society and,
of course, the transition from the old world order to the
new era will not happen overnight. Simplicity itself is
sometimes mocked and if you don't possess the latest

items of fashion or have a life full of activity, this is often considered to be a negative aspect of your personality. Moving from one mind set to another, however, is a process, a journey for the individual to take, and meanwhile you will have to put up with the world being in a state of adolescence.

Thankfully, all teenagers grow into adults and with adulthood usually comes more mature thinking. On the surface it may not be apparent that we live in a society where morals run amok and people make life choices that are contrary to what God wants for us as humans because we are constantly told, particularly by the media, that it is acceptable to be self-indulgent. Have you ever read a magazine and felt lured by the glossy pages into thinking differently about a topic? Words and airbrushed images in collaboration with 'tabloid' styles of writing are very powerful in enticing you, the consumer, either into purchasing items you do not actually need or agreeing with concepts that you do not actually believe. If you followed some of the current advice in magazines you could not only endanger the progress of your journey to shiny, happy health but your soul. Not healthy!

I have read articles that claim that backbiting is conducive to a healthy life alongside reports that a glass of red wine is essential for a healthy heart. Reading such things with the writings of Bahá'u'lláh in mind can be really confusing and it is often very difficult to filter out what is not needed and to embrace what is. You would think that as we evolve and the years pass by that we humans would adopt purer ways of thinking yet only the other day I read that we should gossip with our friends. It did go on to say in that it was bad karma to backbite but then the piece was completed with 'But do it anyway'.

It is an uphill struggle for any Bahá'í to filter out the 'junk' and adopt what is going to be good for one's mind, body and soul but if you constantly strive towards this as a goal, you will enjoy better health. 'Health in the form of simplicity' need not only apply to your diet but to all aspects of life. If you are wondering how gossiping relates to physical vitality, think again about a time in your life when you realized that somebody, perhaps a friend of yours, said words about you that were offensive and perhaps not even true. When you discovered that your friend had said such things when not in your presence, how did you feel? I have been in a similar situation and I remember feeling sick to the stomach, anxious and nervous around that particular friend. Interestingly enough, however, it was feeling that way that reminded me that I should also watch what I say about people.

It is not healthy for us, spiritually or physically, to talk about people and concern ourselves with their everyday affairs, yet we do and this behaviour is advocated by the very tools that promise to help us make the difficult transition from teenage to adulthood – the magazines I was talking about earlier.

I am not saying for one moment that all magazines are bad for you (although actually, a lot of them are!) and that you shouldn't read them, as they also often have good, informative articles, but you do need to be aware of filtering. Do you believe everything you read or are you willing to consider each claim logically then investigate and eventually make up your own mind at the end of your pondering?

An Example

As part of my research for writing this book, I read a variety of 'health' magazines that are overtly directed towards women. The glossy pages are usually adorned with tanned, slender models, all looking the picture of health, while the remaining pages incorporate adverts for make-up and beauty products, all promising to make you younger, firmer, slimmer, prettier, more bronze – and the list continues. Oh, and there are a few articles that, yes, are good to read and are sometimes even informative but you have to find these 'hidden extras' amidst the products and adverts.

Magazines are very clever at conveying that 'this is what "health" looks like and it is available to you in bottles and potions, which by the way, cost a very large amount of money if you were to use all of them and continually'. High-heeled shoes are reported to be in fashion and then there is an advert for corn plasters and blister dressings on the next page that informs us that 'yes, fashionable shoes win over the sensible ones every time but there is sadly a price to pay'. Heels are often worn for the sake of fashion and because women are informed that they are 'in' – the power of suggestion. Women run the inevitable risk not just of blisters but of severe foot deformity in older age because of the unnatural shapes into which their feet are forced. And the slogan attached to the advert to aid the blisters to heal once you have made your 'informed' choice of footwear? 'We make fashion as painless as possible!'

I don't want to get into equality issues in this book – individual choices in life are very important – but just for the sake of the health connection, why do we allow ourselves to suffer the painful consequences of our choices? Doesn't that insult your intelligence even a little bit? Why don't men wear high heels? Why do women? Is it purely because they look 'nice'? I wore high heels to a wedding some years back, determined to give them a fair trial. Nearly all my friends had them and I did quite like the look of them. However, after enduring them for an hour, my feet hurt so much that I could not walk properly for the rest of the day. I decided then that I would not make the effort to get used to wearing these heels – I would instead continue to be happy at my natural height and enjoy healthy, pain free feet.

It is, of course, completely a personal choice and there is no law forbidding the wearing of high heels. This is just a good example of how, if you move more towards simplicity and away from where your passions lie, you will lessen illness and suffering. Remember, if we resist the temptation to indulge ourselves overmuch we won't need to treat our symptoms.

If this seems like a lecture, well, it sort of is. But it is just as much for my benefit as anybody else's. I often fail to consider the consequences of my actions as much as I should and feel that now is the time to contemplate changing some areas of my life – for the greater good!

Activity

Here is an activity that is very useful for inspiring change. You will need pen and paper.

Write down four aspects of your life which, if you changed them, would bring you instant relief.

Here is a personal example:

> I used to drink lots of coffee because I loved the taste! However, I would experience a lot of discomfort as a result of my coffee-drinking – stomach cramps, sharp abdominal pains and poor skin tone. I had an allergy test once and was told that coffee was like poison to my body, hence the severe symptoms. Yet, because I loved the taste and the whole 'Oh, let's go have coffee!' concept, I continued to drink it. Eventually I decided that my pain just wasn't worth it. I stopped drinking coffee, enjoyed better health and stopped pursuing a passion that was leading nowhere.

Even writing this example down has helped me further to realize the extent to which we are in control of our lives but how much we choose to ignore. Taking a few minutes to assess yourself and your habits could gain you many years of health in the long term.

> ... the principal causes of disease are physical, for the human body is composed of numerous elements, but in the measure of an especial equilibrium. As long as this equilibrium is maintained, man is preserved from disease; but if this essential balance, which is the pivot of the constitution, is disturbed, the constitution is disordered, and disease will supervene.
>
> *'Abdu'l-Bahá*[2]

5

Moderation is the Key

I'll just have a small piece
. . . of the cherry

But man hath perversely continued to serve his lustful appetites, and he would not content himself with simple foods. Rather, he prepared for himself food that was compounded of many ingredients, of substances differing one from the other. With this, and with the perpetrating of vile and ignoble acts, his attention was engrossed, and he abandoned the temperance and moderation of a natural way of life. The result was the engendering of diseases both violent and diverse.

'Abdu'l-Bahá[1]

When you look at the menu in a cafe or restaurant, you are faced with various choices. Sometimes you might think of these as 'dilemmas' instead, as the diet you are following determines what you can and cannot choose from the list of temptation. There are always dishes full of ingredients promising to tantalize your tastebuds in ways that can only be achieved by combining lots of different foods together – ones which will possibly, if not probably, leave you reaching for the indigestion tablets later on. There is occasionally a 'healthy option' section, which consists of salads, and the vegetarian choice, which is generally an over-cooked vegetable burger or vegetarian lasagne – I am a vegetarian, so I know the score only too well.

My general observation from the eating habits of my family and friends (as well as my own) is that we tend to gorge ourselves on a variety of the choices on the menu, using the excuse that 'this is a once in a month treat' or 'it's a special occasion'. You may think nothing of consuming a starter (after which you are perhaps a little full but you know there are more culinary delights to sample), the main course, dessert, a possible tray of cheese and crackers and certainly coffee and chocolates, depending on the style of restaurant you care to dine in.

This 'feasting' will inevitably take place in one sitting and the entire experience will probably take less than one hour. If you go to the sort of restaurants that I tend to frequent, they play fast, upbeat music that encourages you to eat at an increased tempo – and the chances are that you will forget to chew half your food.

Question: How will you feel, physically, after this encounter?

a) Happy and energetic.

b) Tired and bloated.

c) None of the above have ever applied to you because you always eat your food carefully, in moderation and only the one course.

I really cannot imagine that many of you have answered a or c, although I am sure that there is a small percentage of people who manage to eat healthily all the time.

My answer would have once been b, as restaurants and cafes, for some reason, encourage my eating habits to misbehave. I would leave the restaurant, top button of trousers undone, feeling I was going to burst at the seams, publicly vowing that I would never, under any circumstances, eat like that again. However, at the next expedition to a restaurant for a 'treat' or 'special occasion', my hunger and taste buds would overcome any rational thinking. And all the memories of pain and uncomfortable feelings? Completely vanished.

So the cycle continues and it is so difficult to break out of it.

I am not suggesting here that you never dine out again and I realize that I am grossly generalizing but what I am asking you to do, as an experiment, is think before you put yourself through the gruelling experience the next time an opportunity arises. Think to yourself, 'I have options here. I am in full control of my choices.'

My workshops focus quite sharply but also inadvertently on the concept of self-discipline. When teaching dance movements, I encourage my students to become aware that every move they make is a direct consequence of they themselves moving that body part. If I say to them, 'Clap your hands three times and then stamp your left foot', their brains will intercept this information and they will attempt to master the sequence. I put them in complete control of all their actions. Later on in the series of workshops, I introduce the idea that we always have a choice about the way we operate in this world, as human beings are endowed with free will. We choose whether we will smoke, drink, actively disobey or adhere to laws and rules . . . and also what makes up our diet.

What you need to try and implement into your daily

routine is this concept of self-discipline and realize that *all* your actions will inevitably require an effect. If you smoke, then your health and people around you will suffer. If you backbite, you injure others and your own soul. If you overeat and neglect your health needs, perhaps exercising no sense of moderation, you will become a slave to your own desires. You will become overweight, be more tired and sluggish and, as a direct result of this self-indulgence, you will not be able to reach your highest potential. Feel empowered to say 'no' when your body does not want to eat or drink and perhaps you will be one step closer to enjoying better health.

Activity

Imagine you are preparing for a dinner party. You are inviting both vegetarians and meat-eaters. Construct a menu that will satisfy the appetites of your guests but will also leave them feeling comfortable and light! (Tip: If you need some helpful hints, you might want to refer to chapter 14.)

Refer back to the quotation at the beginning of this chapter in which 'Abdu'l-Bahá speaks about eating simply and not preparing dishes that use a large number of ingredients.

As an added activity (if you have the time and the money), actually hold this dinner party and make a note of the results. After the meal, ask your guests how they feel physically as a result of eating simply.

It is making slight adjustments such as this that

will eventually become habits and in turn will induce improved health. Having a dinner party for friends can also provide excellent teaching opportunities. Just through your example, your friends will see that there are differences in you without you having to say a word. Not serving alcohol is always a conversation starter for me, as people either already know I am a Bahá'í or they want to know why there are only non-alcoholic beverages to drink. Many of my friends and guests have found the differences very refreshing and, of course, with great dinner conversation, you can't go wrong!

> Between material things and spiritual things there is a connection. The more healthful his body the greater will be the power of the spirit of man; the power of the intellect, the power of the memory, the power of reflection will then be greater.
>
> *'Abdu'l-Bahá*[2]

6

Cows Versus Mothers

The child must, from the day of his birth, be provided with whatever is conducive to his health; and
know ye this: so far as possible, the mother's milk
is best for, more agreeable and better suited to, the
child, unless she should fall ill or her milk should
run entirely dry.

'Abdu'l-Bahá[1]

This chapter is aimed primarily at people who may feel
that they are either lactose intolerant or have always had
a sneaking suspicion that dairy products contribute to a
whole host of common maladies, such as constant colds,
eczema and throat problems. It is also aimed at everyone
else for something to chew over! Having a keen interest in healing through diet and lifestyle means that I am
always investigating alternatives. For the people who
feel that dairy products are not necessary for health, it is
imperative that other options are available. It is essential
for us humans to have sufficient amounts of calcium and
protein in our diets but from which source they come is
up to the individual and in what quantities remains to
be seen, requiring scientific research and further study
of the question.

On a personal level, I have discovered that through
eliminating dairy from my diet, eczema is no longer a
problem for me and I hardly ever suffer from colds and
coughs. I do, however, ensure that my diet is full of calcium-rich foods such as green leafy vegetables, figs, dates,
raw nuts and sesame seeds. There are also more soya
products on the shelves in superstores these days along

with calcium-enriched fresh orange juices. Not everyone's body will react in the same way to dairy so it is important to investigate and find out what suits your body and what is disagreeable to you. It is interesting to note, though, that according to Health Mart Pharmacies, 70 to 90 per cent of those of Asian, African, Native American and Mediterranean descent are intolerant to the lactose in dairy products. It may be an important step for some to at least look into the ever-growing research on this issue.

What is the Weaning Process For?

I once read that human beings are the only species on the planet who are weaned off their mother's milk and have it replaced with another type of milk. If you consider the purpose of any mammal's milk, it is naturally produced to feed the young of the species, containing vital nutrients to encourage growth and development and to promote and enhance a good immune system. However, as soon as a mammal is weaned off its mother's milk, it then starts to eat whatever foods there are in its natural habitat. Cows, for instance, will instinctively eat the grass that grows around them and it provides them with everything they need. Have you ever seen a fully-grown cow drinking milk from its weary mother for its daily nutrition? I haven't either. So why do we drink so much milk as if our lives depended upon it?

Habit?
Misinformation?

Advertising?
Tradition?

These four words can be challenged but there are, of
course, whole countries that do not have any dairy
production yet their inhabitants are fit and active and,
apparently, a lot healthier than people who include a lot
of dairy produce in their diet. In the year 2000, the BBC
News announced online[2] that according to the World
Health Organization, the Japanese are the healthiest
nation in the world yet they do not consume dairy products in the way we do in the West. Britain, for example,
ranks lower in the survey of healthy countries, coming
in at 14 but you would expect it to be healthier. If milk
were that essential for our well-being, it would surely
promote better health.

Many people find cow's milk to be very mucous-
forming and that it contributes to a whole host of diverse
health problems for them. Others may read this and
think, 'What is she talking about? I have never encountered any problems – I am as fit as a fiddle and I drink
two pints of milk every day!' If you are reading this, however, and thinking, 'I always have colds and coughs and
consume a lot of dairy,' you might consider cutting out
dairy for a month and see if there is any improvement.
Either way, it is your own choice – you may benefit from
consuming fewer dairy products or you may not.

Deep discussions with friends on this topic always
tend to be quite controversial. I put this down to 'foundation shaking'. If someone has followed a certain idea

or principle all of his life only to have it challenged or even proved wrong, it shakes his very foundation. I am not completely 'anti-dairy' and recognize that milk does have many nutritional qualities, which can be beneficial to health. I even have a milky hot chocolate now and then and the odd pizza with a cheesy stuffed crust. My body doesn't shut down when I do this but I do usually get a pressure build-up in my sinuses and sometimes spend the subsequent day sneezing and blowing my nose. However, this doesn't mean all and sundry will also react in this way.

However, this is not my point. Human beings are very capable of living, and very healthily too, without consuming any dairy products. Eczema was the bane of my teenage years and I wish I had known this information sooner. I had the mind set that if didn't have at least two servings of dairy foods a day, I would probably get brittle bones or just wither away and die. Of course, not everyone will have the same reactions to dairy and you may find that cow's milk agrees with you perfectly well (especially if it is accompanied by a plateful of warm cookies!) but it is not essential for our survival.

Many people maintain that humans are meant to drink cow's milk and that if you don't you will become ill and calcium deficient. I won't go into the scientific reasons that demonstrate how humans are *not* designed for excessive milk consumption; I am going to stick with the simplest 'argument'. 'Abdu'l-Bahá says that the best milk for a child is its mother's – it is 'more agreeable' and 'better suited' and there must be a wisdom behind this. Calcium can be obtained from other foods such as green leafy vegetables, raw nuts, raw sesame seeds and many fruits and grains. Maybe what needs to be observed here is moderation. You don't have to forsake your Ben and Jerry's and Haagen Daaz completely! Just consider though – how do cows themselves obtain calcium for their big bovine bones? Is it through a 'healthy' daily allowance of milk, or through chewing the cud and chomping the grains?

Challenge

If you suffer from
- Headaches
- Persistent colds or allergies
- Arthritis
- Hay fever
- Asthma

and feel that dairy *may* be the problem, then try to reduce or even completely avoid dairy products for a month but ensure that you introduce other calcium-rich foods into your diet. I have mentioned a few suggestions already but here is the list again with a few additions and even then it's not exhaustive. After all, it is important that your diet is varied and balanced, with or without cow juice!

- Tofu
- Sardines (with bones)
- Legumes

- Baked beans
- Pak choi
- Turnip greens
- Calcium fortified orange juice
- Soy beans
- Kidney beans
- Broccoli
- Figs and dates
- Leafy greens

Try to reduce or even completely avoid dairy products. I am not saying that there is a 100 per cent certainty that your problems will all disappear as there may be other contributing factors to your illnesses but you may discover, as I did, that the triggers for these ailments lie in the consumption of too much dairy! You can only discover new truths if you investigate! If, however, dairy is not a problem for you in any way, shape or form, then perhaps you could still investigate the pros and cons of eliminating it from your diet so as to understand why others may need to do this. Dairy intolerance is often met by human intolerance, especially when others have not suffered in the same way.

> Although ill health is one of the unavoidable conditions of man, truly it is hard to bear. The bounty of good health is the greatest of all gifts.
>
> *'Abdu'l-Bahá*[3]

7

Food of the Future

The cow is saying to a human, 'Do you know that
your species used to eat us?'
The human replies, 'No, I heard that was just a
vicious rumour.'

'What will be the food of the future?' 'Fruit and grains. The time will come when meat will no longer be eaten. Medical science is only in its infancy, yet it has shown that our natural diet is that which grows out of the ground. The people will gradually develop up to the condition of this natural food.'

'Abdu'l-Bahá[1]

This quotation will alleviate the anxiety of the avid meat-eater. After reading this book, you do not have to renounce all meat eating. There is no law, no obligation and no expectation but we are told of a certainty that, in the future, meat will no longer be eaten. We can only assume that this does not mean the time we are living in now, as we have a vast meat production and animal products are widely available across the globe. Alongside this fact, vegetarianism and all the promotion that accompanies it is definitely on the increase. Look at how many health scares and connections to serious diseases are associated with the consumption of animal products. Bahá'ís must at least support the imminent changes, which cannot be ignored, as this is preparation for our future – it is inescapable! When friends and family ask me if I have to be a vegetarian as part of my religion, I say, 'No, but it says in the Bahá'í writings that there will be a time when we live on a diet completely free of meat. This is my personal choice but not all Bahá'ís are vegetarians.'

If you find a world without eating meat hard to imagine, if you think, 'That's impossible! Where will all the animals go?' perhaps you will consider the past and the amazing changes that have been made. When I talk to my younger students about the roots of gum boot dancing, which originated at a time when people were treated as slaves in the mines, they can barely comprehend even the concept! Some of my students don't even believe what I tell them. How could it possibly have been that people were not allowed to communicate with one another and were beaten or killed if they did? It is completely unreal to them, as unreal as fairies and Santa. King William IV abolished slavery in 1833 in England and nowadays people in the West find it hard to imagine that humans could have been bought and sold and treated abominably as part of the normal course of things – although we know that even today slavery exists in some parts of the world. There was also a time when many people thought that the earth was flat! But look at how our understandings have changed and modified through the ages because of our increased knowledge and incredible scientific discoveries. People in the future will read about civilization as we know it now and think, 'I can't believe they used to eat meat! How strange is that?'

To prepare ourselves for this new way of thinking, we can just be aware that others may want to follow these counsels now and we can support them in their efforts. The next chapter will discuss just how we can do this.

Arise thou to serve God and help His Cause. He, verily, will assist thee with the hosts of the seen and unseen . . .

Bahá'u'lláh[2]

8

From the Beginning of Time

I got tofu and salad on rye bread

> Regarding the eating of animal flesh and abstinence therefrom, know thou of a certainty that, in the beginning of creation, God determined the food of every living being, and to eat contrary to that determination is not approved.
>
> 'Abdu'l-Bahá[1]

Let me make it clear that the purpose of these chapters is not to persuade you to become a vegetarian! I have included them so that you can be aware of what the teachings say and then make your own personal choices.

The 'vegetarian debate' is certainly an interesting one. When I was a teenager, I watched a programme in which the presenter went undercover to investigate an abattoir in Britain. From that point on I became a vegetarian, although, arguably, not a 'proper' one as I still ate fish. This was purely for 'animal rights' reasons and had nothing to do with my diet. The programme appealed to my caring emotions and inspired me to change something that I had been accustomed to ever since I could remember.

Not eating meat, however, does not necessarily mean that you will enjoy greater health – this is an assumption many people make: stop eating meat, become a healthy person. I know quite a few vegetarians who are many pounds overweight and who still suffer from common ailments such as colds and coughs. It is not simply eradicating meat from your diet that will ensure you are a healthy human – you will need to take a more holistic approach and consider other areas of your diet and lifestyle, working out through trial and error what your body responds to well and what it repels.

Even though my family were supportive of my individual choices, I encountered many people who found it difficult that I did not eat animal flesh. Now, as an older and slightly wiser person, I do not take such disparagement to heart, as people who criticize tend to have their own insecurities and, of course, are entitled to their opinion. But I often found myself at the centre of debates, being verbally attacked for my personal views. 'Why do so many people care whether I eat meat or not?' I used to wonder.

Nowadays, I am a vegetarian for a combination of reasons, one of them being that I have decided that the eating of meat is contrary to what I have been designed as a human being to consume and, as 'Abdu'l-Bahá states, 'to eat contrary to that determination is not approved'.

My main test with being a vegetarian has been with those who have found reasons to disagree with this individual choice. I have been in discussion with friends who thought that the Bahá'í writings mention that humans are meant to eat meat now but that in the future our bodies will have evolved to the state of non-meat-eaters. However, if we look closely at the words of the Master, He counsels – not instructs – that to eat meat is 'contrary' to what we are intended to eat. We see that 'in the beginning of creation', God determined the appropriate food for every living creature.

Many of my friends not only eat meat but also wholly advocate its consumption. A parallel can be drawn with smoking. As Baháʼís we are not explicitly forbidden to smoke but the writings state very clearly that this is contrary to what God wants for us. Surely you would not exhort others to smoke, saying that even though it is contrary to what God wants for us, we can still do it. The point with this is that you *can* eat meat if you want to and need to but it is better for you if you don't. Baháʼís should be the most encouraging people to those who want to adopt this counsel. There is nothing in the Baháʼí writings that forbids us to eat meat but we are told that it would 'undoubtedly be better' and 'more pleasing' to content ourselves with other foods.[2]

For the vegetarians and vegans reading this, there may be times when you will be conversing with your friends and they will assure you that people should eat meat now and lots of it (it does, after all, taste really good). It is fine to hold personal opinions but it is always a good idea to check out what the writings say about such matters. ʻAbduʼl-Bahá provides insights into why humans have never been and never will be natural meat-eaters. I find it fascinating to read this, considering that at the time it was written, being a vegetarian in the West was not so easy as it is today. There was no 'Linda McCartney' range and vegeburgers and fake bacon were certainly not in the freezer compartments in superstores.

> . . . beasts of prey, such as the wolf, lion and leopard, are endowed with ferocious, tearing instruments, such as hooked talons and claws. From this it is evident that the food of such beasts is meat. If they

69

were to attempt to graze, their teeth would not cut the grass, neither could they chew the cud, for they do not have molars. Likewise, God hath given to the four-footed grazing animals such teeth as reap the grass like a sickle, and from this we understand that the food of these species of animal is vegetable. They cannot chase and hunt down other animals. The falcon hath a hooked beak and sharp talons; the hooked beak preventeth him from grazing, therefore his food is also meat.

But now coming to man, we see he hath neither hooked teeth nor sharp nails or claws, nor teeth like iron sickles. From this it becometh evident and manifest that the food of man is cereals and fruit. Some of the teeth of man are like millstones to grind the grain, and some are sharp to cut the fruit. Therefore he is not in need of meat, nor is he obliged to eat it. Even without eating meat he would live with the utmost vigour and energy. For example, the community of the Brahmins in India do not eat meat; notwithstanding this they are not inferior to other nations in strength, power, vigour, outward senses or intellectual virtues. Truly, the killing of animals and the eating of their meat is somewhat contrary to pity and compassion, and if one can content himself with cereals, fruit, oil and nuts, such as pistachios, almonds and so on, it would undoubtedly be better and more pleasing.

'Abdu'l-Bahá[3]

I remember reading an article in the United Kingdom *Bahá'í Journal* a few years back written by a woman who had read about the 'food of the future' and had tried to live, unsuccessfully, on a diet of just fruit and grains. Medical science continues to progress and we need to remember that everybody is different when it comes to diet and eating patterns. For example, my diet at present consists mainly of cereals, grains, fruit, raw salad and vegetables and I have never felt healthier! But if drastic changes are made suddenly instead of gradually, such changes, which will eventually become your way of eating, could be of more harm than help. Changes in my diet have been introduced slowly into my daily routine over the years – not overnight. Be sensible about it, consult perhaps with friends, a trusted doctor or dietitian and read around the subject. There is a list of suggested and recommended reading at the end of this book so use your resources and decide what is right for you. You don't *have* to give up eating meat, fish and poultry but if you do *and* you eat wisely, then you should enjoy better health.

Teeth

But why do we have teeth then? Surely we have sharp teeth to rip the meat apart?

This is always an interesting point, which crops up in many vegetarian debates. However, 'Abdu'l-Bahá says that, from the beginning of time, our food has been determined for us and it has never been meat. That is not to say that you can't eat meat but if you consider how true carnivores eat flesh, they certainly don't buy it from Tesco's, all ready-packed and treated for human consumption. Your teeth can cope with chewing cooked meats and sometimes even raw, if that's your preference, but when did you last see a zebra and have an uncontrollable urge to attack and rip it apart limb from limb? Hopefully, never! It is not our natural instinct to kill in the same way as some animals have an inherent design to do so for their survival. 'Abdu'l-Bahá gives the following insights into the true function of the human tooth:

> Thou hast written regarding the four canine teeth in man, saying that these teeth, two in the upper jaw and two in the lower, are for the purpose of eating meat. Know thou that these four teeth are not created for meat-eating, although one can eat meat with them. All the teeth of man are made for eating fruit, cereals and vegetables. These four teeth, however, are designed for breaking hard shells, such as those of almonds. But eating meat is not forbidden or unlawful, nay, the point is this, that it is possible for man to live without eating meat and still be strong.[4]

Note how 'Abdu'l-Bahá says that even though the teeth are not designed for meat-eating, it is not forbidden and unlawful to eat meat. You can eat a quarter-pounder if you wish without feeling as if you are doing something wrong. One of the stories told about 'Abdu'l-Bahá describes how He reportedly offered meat to a pilgrim. The pilgrim politely refused, saying he was a vegetarian. 'Abdu'l-Bahá was said to have exclaimed, 'But it's good for you!'

Meat is not devoid of nutrients; it is just not necessary for our survival.

There may even be times when eating meat is wise for other reasons. For example, I lived out in a rural village in Swaziland, southeast Africa, for a few weeks, while on a year of service. During this time our diet consisted mainly of rice, bread and sometimes meat. It would have been highly rude of me to turn down any offers of food while living on this homestead – the family had few possessions, survived on weekly water rations and worked extremely hard to obtain any food in the first place.

To prepare myself for this situation, I stopped being a vegetarian before going to live in Africa as a friend who had lived there previously advised me that there would certainly be situations where meat was offered and where the concept of being a vegetarian was not understood. His advice stemmed from personal experience, as he hadn't prepared his body for eating animal flesh beforehand and had to politely endure eating liver when he had not eaten meat for years. Sometimes meat may be the only food available, or it is offered to you as a guest of honour, so to avoid offending, or going hungry, think ahead! The Universal House of Justice explained to an individual:

Here too, as in all other things, the believers should

73

be conscious of the two principles of moderation and courtesy in the way they express their opinions and in deciding whether they should refuse food offered to them or request special food.

There are, of course, instances where a believer would be fully justified in abstaining from or eating only certain foods for some medical reason, but this is a different matter and would be understood by any reasonable person.[5]

As I become more aware of my eating habits and how my body responds to food, I feel less inclined to label myself as a vegetarian or vegan. I am not going to rule out the possibility that I may never eat animal products again so do I need to pigeonhole myself into a category which sometimes can be divisive rather than constructive? If you don't want to call yourself a vegetarian, this doesn't mean you have to eat barrel loads of meat to compensate. Eating a simple diet with few animal products will be beneficial to your health – regardless of whether or not you attach a title to this choice.

> It is certain . . . that if man can live on a purely vegetarian diet and thus avoid killing animals, it would be much preferable.
>
> *Shoghi Effendi*[6]

9

Healing Illnesses with Foods

Take 2 a day with a glass of water

The Báb hath said that the people of Bahá must develop the science of medicine to such a high degree that they will heal illnesses by means of foods. The basic reason for this is that if, in some component substance of the human body, an imbalance should occur, altering its correct, relative proportion to the whole, this fact will inevitably result in the onset of disease. If, for example, the starch component should be unduly augmented, or the sugar component decreased, an illness will take control. It is the function of a skilled physician to determine which constituent of his patient's body hath suffered diminution, which hath been augmented. Once he hath discovered this, he must prescribe a food containing the diminished element in considerable amounts, to re-establish the body's essential equilibrium. The patient, once his constitution is again in balance, will be rid of his disease.

'Abdu'l-Bahá[1]

My mind creaks under the weight of considering this particular piece of writing – first because it needs careful studying owing to the complexities it offers the reader and second because it shares with us such an amazing bounty. How is this I hear you cry? Well, for me when I read this passage (and I had to read it quite a few times to get my head round it!) it seems a groundbreaking concept that such simple yet incredible scientific progress will enable skilled and competent physicians to treat illnesses through our diet! At the moment, the medical profession is just scratching the surface of investigating the science of medicine but with time there will be an expansion to this marvellous understanding that if there is an imbalance in our body, and we suffer an illness because of this imbalance, food of the correct proportions and correct nutrients will be given to us in order to become well again. I find it pretty astounding and yet also intriguing that the answers to many of our illnesses are lying right within our reach but we have to discover them first and increase our awareness and understanding of how illnesses can be healed by means of foods.

Before we move on, I would like you to take a moment to digest the quotation – no pun intended! It is full of words that not everyone will understand so I have chosen the ones that I needed to clarify for my own understanding and have provided you with a mini-glossary below. Once you have read the definitions and have taken in their meaning, I suggest that you read the passage two or three more times, in your head and spoken out loud.

Component – part of a whole

Imbalance – lack of balance

Augmented – increased or enlarged

Constituent – forming part of a whole

Diminution – make less or smaller

Equilibrium – steadiness or stability

After reading the passage several times, you should have a deeper understanding. If you still find it difficult to comprehend, try and explain it to someone else as if you were a teacher. Role play can sometimes help to gain increased knowledge of a subject that you find difficult. Now we can move on to the last part of the quotation. 'Abdu'l-Bahá says:

> At whatever time highly-skilled physicians shall have developed the healing of illnesses by means of foods, and shall make provision for simple foods, and shall prohibit humankind from living as slaves to their lustful appetites, it is certain that the incidence of chronic and diversified illnesses will abate, and the general health of all mankind will be much improved. This is destined to come about.
>
> *'Abdu'l-Bahá*[2]

Again, how comforting! To me, these words signify the change from old world order to new! This concept, this *reality* of healing illnesses with food, is 'destined to come about', so as medical science increases in its knowledge and understanding of the human body and disease, so shall the development of this highly important principle. Yet we also have our part to play and this means eating simply and not becoming slaves to our tastebuds. It may also mean that foods we once considered to be healthy we may need to cut down on or renounce altogether in order to obtain optimum health. It's all about being well-informed and really listening to your body, while also consulting professionals as well as using a mind set of logic. Can you imagine a world in which illnesses were few and far between and where humans were so clued up about their bodies that they wouldn't even have the inclination to eat or drink products that were harmful? 'Abdu'l-Bahá says that if we *do* 'make provision for simple foods' then 'the general health of all mankind will be much improved'. How exciting, that even though this is *destined* to come about, we can make choices which will help us draw nearer to this goal *right now*.

There is yet more solace to be had, as 'Abdu'l-Bahá also counsels that;

> The majority of the diseases which overtake man also overtake the animal, but the animal is not cured by drugs. In the mountains, as in the wilderness, the animal's physician is the power of taste and smell. The sick animal smells the plants that grow in the wilderness; he eats those that are sweet and fragrant to his smell and taste, and is cured. The cause of his healing is this. When the sugar ingredient has become diminished in his constitution, he begins to long for sweet things; therefore, he eats an herb with a sweet taste, for nature urges and guides him; its smell and taste please him and

he eats it. The sugar ingredient in his nature will be increased, and health will be restored.

It is, therefore, evident that it is possible to cure by foods, aliments and fruits; but as today the science of medicine is imperfect, this fact is not yet fully grasped. When the science of medicine reaches perfection, treatment will be given by foods, aliments, fragrant fruits and vegetables, and by various waters, hot and cold in temperature.[3]

Again, something to look forward to and strive towards but also to take heed of today. It may not be that scientists have perfected the art of curing by foods as of yet, but we can still . . .

Look to the cause and not just at the symptoms.

Even though I have touched upon this topic in earlier chapters, I feel it is so important that I will mention it again. From the writings quoted in this chapter it may be evident that in the future it is destined that all illnesses will be healed by foods. However, in *this* day, where obesity is still on the rise and where pills, tonics and medicinal drugs line our shelves even in the supermarkets, how can we improve our quality of life *right now*? It does, after all come back to one major point we looked at earlier – how can we be of service to others if we are ill, sickly, poorly, unwell or, in some cases, literally dying as we have not taken care of ourselves.

Consider this. When you become ill (as with a cold,

cough, skin disorder, lethargy and so on), do you rationalize the illness and think 'Ah! I drank six cups of coffee yesterday so this is why I have a terrible stomach upset today' or do you just get on with it and take as many medicines as possible to eradicate the illness?

Perhaps a balance of both given examples would be wise. If you are ill, then you may certainly need to consult your doctor and he may prescribe you a course of antibiotics or specific pills which will clear up the infection, lessen the cough and make the illness go away. However, this is where seeking out the *cause* comes into play! If you don't find out *why* you are suffering in the first place, then the chances are you will continue to suffer from that illness at some other point in your life. You can't keep taking antibiotics forever and why suffer unnecessarily if you can actually pinpoint what throws your body out of synch? Investigating the *cause* of the illness and not just dealing with the symptoms can make your life so much happier! When a good friend's father discovered that certain foods were contributing to his migraines, he was able to then cut out these products – and the result? He is now pretty much migraine-free! The painkillers he had previously been prescribed were only serving to mask the terrible pain he had to endure. But how much happier was he when the light was shown at the end of a long, arduous tunnel by a practitioner who suggested cutting our certain trigger foods? The answer of course is *very* happy. It is a joyous feeling when you realize that you can improve your health by your own volition. It's almost as if someone gives you a pair of eyeglasses and everything becomes a lot clearer. It's not easy – it's a process and sometimes it's hard to give up the things you love – in my case, it was a bowl of a favourite brand of cereal, a massive milkshake at McDonald's, pasta covered in cheese and a hot chocolate every night before bed – but when you weigh up your health against your taste-buds, you realize that it's such a small sacrifice to make.

Here's a challenge for you to try. The next time you fall ill, or even experience discomfort like heartburn or feeling bloated after a meal, think about what you eat generally and assess the data. If you want to determine the cause of an illness, seek out a professional who can help you analyse what you eat and drink. It may even be that it's not *what* you eat but *when* in the day you eat it, *how* you prepare it and in what quantities. Again, I will include the books that I have read on these subjects which I have found to be saving graces in my life. You may not agree with everything that's written out there but at least you can kick-start yourself on a road to recovery – if you need to, that is!

This is about readdressing the balance and listening to what your body needs. If you feel unable to do this alone, ask for assistance. You must always consult physicians in times of illness but if you start seeking out the *causes* of everyday ailments, you will benefit yourself in the long term. Living a simpler life, as discussed, will certainly help. Overloading your body with the junk of today is responsible for many illnesses which are too varied and complex to mention here. Again, if you look to the animal kingdom for advice, you can perhaps learn that simplicity and moderation are key factors, not just for mere survival but for great health and well-being. Isn't it something to think about that even though our spiritual station is higher than that of the animal, we still have a wealth of information to learn from these contented creatures!

> For the animal, as to its body, is made up of the same constituent elements as man. Since, however, the animal contenteth itself with simple foods and striveth not to indulge its importunate urges to any great degree, and commiteth no sins, its ailments relative to man's are few.
>
> *'Abdu'l-Bahá*[4]

10

The Most Harmful Counter-Health Choices

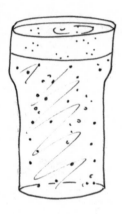

O ye, God's loved ones! Experience hath shown how greatly the renouncing of smoking, of intoxicating drink, and of opium, conduceth to health and vigour, to the expansion and keenness of the mind and to bodily strength. There is today a people who strictly avoid tobacco, intoxicating liquor and opium. This people is far and away superior to the others, for strength and physical courage, for health, beauty and comeliness.

'Abdu'l-Bahá[1]

After much deliberation, I have decided to add a chapter that considers the harmful effects of alcohol, drugs and smoking. All are touchy areas to young Bahá'ís, especially those who move in mainly 'non-Bahá'í' circles, and although they are not 'foods' *per se*, they are certainly consumed in vast quantities. And as 'Abdu'l-Bahá so poignantly states, renouncing these vices (giving them up!) will greatly improve your health and in turn your spirituality.

Again, these are issues people are faced with on a daily basis. When you are at school, university, college or the workplace, the majority of people will drink alcohol and a further number will smoke and take drugs. Many people's lives are centred on taking or using these vices, which is why it is sometimes difficult to take the alternative path. The major obstacle here for some Bahá'ís is that in renouncing drinking and smoking you are seen as being different from everyone else. On the one hand, being different is 'cool' but sometimes it can also make you the odd one out, with the possibility of alienating you from your group.

As a Bahá'í, however, you know deep down what the Central Figures have to say about these subjects. Nevertheless, there is what seems to be an eternal conflict between your higher and lower selves. This is where that great tool 'self-discipline' comes into play. It enables you not only to follow the laws of Bahá'u'lláh but also to use your reason and listen to logic. Your mind set will largely orchestrate how you deal with the pressure of deciding whether to put these substances into your body, substances which not only damage your general health but can also kill you with prolonged usage!

Alcohol

When I was a pupil at school I was fortunate to have a close group of friends who were not interested in drinking and smoking so I found it easier not to engage in these so-called social pleasures. Having graced a few end of term parties, witnessing many tears, fights, people unable to communicate rationally owing to being highly intoxicated, blood poisoning, vomiting, more tears and horrific headaches the next morning, not to mention the embarrassment and sheer anxiety of 'who slept with whom' and 'I could be pregnant', was enough to put me off alcohol and, eventually, led me to stop drinking altogether. Just think how many of these dire situations could be completely avoided, even eradicated if we did not succumb to so much pressure.

However, this does not mean that I sailed through the earlier days of my life without my own tests and challenges and that I used reason and logic to overcome them! Friends and family had their own advice to give and, of course, society's lax laws make it very easy to get into a situation where you end up consuming alcohol.

Growing up in a non-Bahá'í family presents its own tests and challenges – you want to follow the laws of Bahá'u'lláh and you strive to be a 'good Bahá'í' but you are faced with constant opposition – your beliefs may seriously challenge what your family or friends deem to be acceptable and they might not understand why it is important for you to follow these laws, especially if they do not accept Bahá'u'lláh as the Manifestation of God for this day and age. This, however, is a test. There are very good reasons why laws are there – they are for your freedom and protection. If drinking alcohol was good for humans and never created any problems in society, there would be no reason to prohibit it. But all you need to do is spend half an hour with a lifetime alcoholic or witness the breakdown of an entire community to real-ize how it destroys not only your mind and senses but also your entire body. It makes sense not to drink! To take the argument, 'Well, I would drink in moderation' is not good enough. Maybe you would personally but then it is still available for all the people who find it hard to have just the one drink and as a result there is crime, violence, disease and disorder, unwanted pregnancies, addiction and depression.

I have spoken to many Bahá'ís who do not drink but

feel they always have to give the same response when asked if they do. They mumble something inaudible about 'religion', get embarrassed and then their friends think they are strange! Investigate *why* it is not good to drink so you can say with clarity and confidence why you do not want to follow the crowd and get drunk.

For example:

'Hey, we're going out to get wasted on Saturday night – do you want to join us?'

Your choices here are as follows.

1) You say no thanks but don't give a reason.

2) You go and 'get wasted'.

3) You go but you drink coke and orange juice and end up having to look after your friends all night when they are loud and rude (plus, of course, the next day when they are grumpy with headaches suffering from their hangovers), drive them home, knowing that they might make a mess in your car – not much fun for you.

4) You tell them 'I'm a Bahá'í – I don't drink.'

5) You tell them your own logical reason for not drinking: 'I want to be in control of myself at all times'/ 'Do you know how many thousands of people are

affected each year by death and violence in the home in this country alone because of alcohol? I don't want to support a cause such as that! As long as I'm buying it, I am sort of contributing to the problem.'/'Do you know how many calories are in a beer? No thanks, I'm looking after my health!'

6) 'I don't need alcohol to get me high anymore – I can get high on your company/the music/the atmosphere.'

You will always have choices. If you list them all, they are easier to decipher. You decide – your 'health and vigour', 'keenness of the mind' and 'bodily strength' or a wreck on the floor with limited capacity. I feel blessed that my parents were so open and non-restrictive when I was younger – this enabled me to be myself and I didn't have much to rebel against! Don't get me wrong, I wasn't the perfect teenager but I eventually found no need for alcohol. So as well as following a law of Bahá'u'lláh, I was also able to give my own reasons why I didn't drink, should people have asked (and, surprisingly, many of my friends respected me for this).

> It is inadmissible that man, who hath been endowed with reason, should consume that which stealeth it away. Nay, rather it behoveth him to comport himself in a manner worthy of the human station, and not in accordance with the misdeeds of every heedless and wavering soul.
>
> *Bahá'u'lláh*[2]

Smoking

As a non-smoker, I could provide you with many reasons why you shouldn't smoke but I am not going to preach my personal views to you! It is actually up to the individual whether or not to smoke, as it is not specifically prohibited in the writings. You may feel, therefore, that if there is the element of 'free choice', why is it so frowned upon? Some Bahá'í events you may have been to will have enforced a complete ban, while at others organizers will have set up designated areas for smoking. Either way, most Bahá'ís I know feel too ashamed or scared to smoke in front of non-smokers and it seems to be generally unacceptable. However, even though it is not forbidden, there *are* strong warnings in the writings relating to this subject which not only give you more of an insight into *why* smoking is frowned upon but also allows you personal choice, making you rely on your own reasoning, logic and the most scary thing of all – your conscience!

'Abdu'l-Bahá says the following regarding smoking:

> . . . there are . . . forbidden things which do not cause immediate harm, and the injurious effects of which are only gradually produced: such acts are also repugnant to the Lord, and blameworthy in His sight, and repellent. The absolute unlawfulness of these, however, hath not been expressly set forth in the Text, but their avoidance is necessary to purity, cleanliness, the preservation of health, and freedom from addiction.

Among these latter is smoking tobacco, which is dirty, smelly, offensive – an evil habit, and one the harmfulness of which gradually becometh apparent to all. Every qualified physician hath ruled – and this hath also been proven by tests – that one of the components of tobacco is a deadly poison, and that the smoker is vulnerable to many and various diseases. This is why smoking hath been plainly set forth as repugnant from the standpoint of hygiene . . .

My meaning is that in the sight of God, smoking tobacco is deprecated, abhorrent, filthy in the extreme; and, albeit by degrees, highly injurious to health. It is also a waste of money and time, and maketh the user a prey to a noxious addiction. To those who stand firm in the Covenant, this habit is therefore censured both by reason and experience, and renouncing it will bring relief and peace of mind to all men. Furthermore, this will make it possible to have a fresh mouth and unstained fingers, and hair that is free of a foul and repellent smell.

'Abdu'l-Bahá[3]

Having lived with people who smoke, I know how difficult it is to try and give up. However, increased awareness and advertising shows alarmingly how terrible it is for your health and for anyone who breathes in the smoke. If you are inspired to quit, take it one day at a time. Consult the professionals and try and see the bigger picture. Your withdrawal symptoms will not last forever and the health benefits you gain from giving up will be numerous. What's more, it will bring you 'relief and peace of mind'. And that's advantageous to everybody!

Taking Drugs

Although not as socially acceptable, drug-taking is common in today's society and will undoubtedly present itself to you in one way or another, if it hasn't done so already. It would be wrong of me just to assume that no Bahá'í will ever have to face this issue as a test and a challenge as many of my friends have had to make some very difficult choices regarding the use of drugs.

Aside from being highly illegal with the possibility of imprisonment and the death penalty (in some countries) if you are discovered possessing, taking or trafficking drugs, you will seriously damage your health and your spiritual nature if you pursue this avenue. Here is what the Universal House of Justice says:

> Concerning the so-called 'spiritual' virtues of the hallucinogens . . . spiritual stimulation should come from turning one's heart to Bahá'u'lláh, and not through physical means such as drugs and agents.
> . . . As the friends, including the youth, are required strictly to abstain from all forms of intoxicants, and are further expected conscientiously to obey the civil law of their country, it is obvious

that they should refrain from using these drugs.

A very great responsibility for the future peace and well-being of the world is borne by the youth of today. Let the Bahá'í youth by the power of the Cause they espouse be the shining example for their companions.[4]

The last part of this quotation relates directly to the purpose of this book. If the people of the world are looking to the Bahá'ís for their example, what greater example is there than someone who is the picture of health? The well-being of the world depends largely on the well-being of the individual and, as discussed, this stems from personal choices, self-discipline and an acute awareness of the writings, which can guide us gently towards these choices.

> Make ye then a mighty effort, that the purity and sanctity which, above all else, are cherished by 'Abdu'l-Bahá, shall distinguish the people of Bahá; that in every kind of excellence the people of God shall surpass all other human beings; that both outwardly and inwardly they shall prove superior to the rest; that for purity, immaculacy, refinement, and the preservation of health, they shall be leaders in the vanguard of those who know. And that by their freedom from enslavement, their knowledge, their self-control, they shall be first among the pure, the free and the wise.
>
> 'Abdu'l-Bahá[5]

11

Principles in Practice

Wow! Is that the Bahá'í Faith he's got there?

Until the public sees in the Bahá'í community a true pattern, in action, of something better than it already has, it will not respond to the Faith in large numbers.

Shoghi Effendi[1]

When you look at a person, you try not to 'judge a book by its cover'. It is quite a challenge not to do this, however, and as the Bahá'í community comes under increased scrutiny, as the Faith progresses, people will be looking to Bahá'ís for various reasons. You need to consider, 'What can I show them that is different yet appeals to their spiritual capacity and nature?' We are all individuals, which is a great thing – the planet is full of diversity and without it we would be quite the boring race! If we all looked the same, had identical skin colour, hobbies, personality and agendas, we might as well be clones. This, thankfully, is not the case. We have a lot of freedom and options in this life and yet it is sometimes these choices that let us down when it comes to being an example to communities.

As you may have gathered by now, this book is not just about healthy ways of eating: it is about looking after your health as a whole – mind, body and soul – and making choices that are conducive to our own needs, which in turn will be of benefit or service to the needs of humanity. So the question is, where do you start making these improvements and how can you implement them into your already busy life?

Consider 'Abdu'l-Bahá – the perfect example of a

human being. He didn't go round preaching and pros-elytizing to the world about how we should live, He simply *lived* His life in accordance with the Word of God and gently, through love and compassion, allowed us to learn from His example. Using this non-intrusive method people are less likely to be angered and are more inclined to follow your lead. When I taught English in mainstream education, if the class noise levels began to rise and children were becoming unfocused, instead of shouting at them and chastising them for their behav-iour, I would start to speak in very soft, quiet tones, almost in a whisper. Eventually, in a matter of minutes, the noise level would decrease and the children would refocus on the task at hand.

When you respect a person, you may often feel com-pelled to emulate his behaviour, actions and methods and try and live according to his standards. This being the case, if people are looking to others to set standards, then it seems wise to try and improve what you already have so they can look to your standards for guidance. I am not suggesting for one moment that all the peoples of the world are immoral and need to find better codes of behaviour. I have learned lessons and ways of being from all walks of life, cultures, ages, male and female, rich and poor. However, in these turbulent times, it is certainly the case that moral depravity supersedes goodness in our society *at present*. This will undoubtedly alter as time moves on but you need to consider implementing these changes now, as it is a crucial time for Bahá'ís and will be in the foreseeable future. And what better way than to show people a radiant, healthy, spiritually striving person. If I see someone who is the picture of health, I always want to know the secrets of their success. When people ask me why *I* am so happy and radiant I tell them about my ways of eating, my spiritual habits and how I strive at all times to improve myself. The important word here is *strive* because even though you may not always achieve your goals, you can always work towards them and learn from your mistakes.

> The Bahá'í standard is very high, more particularly when compared with the thoroughly rotten morals of the present world. But this standard of ours will produce healthier, happier, nobler people . . .
>
> *Shoghi Effendi*[2]

A great place to start any self-improvement is, of course, with you – the 'number one' we discussed earlier. It is tempting to try and make others go through what you have experienced but they just might not be at the same place as you are. You may want to lose some weight, for example, and perhaps you really want to help a friend who also needs to lose weight for health reasons. If you ask him when he is not ready to take steps for himself, however, it will be hard on you, your friend and possibly your friendship. Make these changes for your own self – it is up to others to improve their habits and ways of being, and remember, you can always be an example to them, which eventually they may want to follow of their own accord.

Ask yourself this question: 'If 'Abdu'l-Bahá were to visit my house this morning, how would I feel?'

I asked myself this very same question once after looking around our living room and seeing a disorganized mess – papers everywhere, empty mugs by the sofa and on the table, bits on the floor. Not only was the house disorganized but my head was in a bit of a state too. If the house is not clean and spruce then my state of mind often reflects this. My answer, therefore, to this question was, 'I would feel too ashamed to let 'Abdu'l-Bahá into my house. I wouldn't want Him to sit on a dirty sofa with tomato stains from the night before and even if He didn't feel uncomfortable, I certainly would!'

Now ask yourself, would you have the same standards for friends, family or people who just happen to call as you would for 'Abdu'l-Bahá? A lady from our street was showing an interest in the Bahá'í Faith and we had conversed generally about the main principles and teachings. One day, she just happened to call out of the blue. I was having a bit of a lazy morning and looked like I'd just got out of bed. Usually I would have invited her in for a cup of tea and impromptu fireside but there was no way I wanted her to see how everything was in such disarray – plates scattered everywhere from last night's dinner, unfiled paper littering the tables and chairs and rings on the floor where mugs of tea had been. Now I know that we don't usually let the house go to ruin like this but here I was, saying that 'now' wasn't a good time to have a chat. What a wasted opportunity! This single experience enticed me into action – our house isn't always picture perfect but we strive harder every day to keep the place clean and looking respectable.

> And although bodily cleanliness is a physical thing, it hath, nevertheless, a powerful influence on the life of the spirit.
>
> *'Abdu'l-Bahá*[3]

> The fact of having a pure and spotless body exercises an influence upon the spirit of man.
>
> *'Abdu'l-Bahá*[4]

You can apply the same line of questioning to other areas in your life and, one by one, you can improve the elements of those things with which you are truly unhappy. I once avoided our cellar for about a month because it was in such a mess. I had a year's worth of filing to sort out and it was all dusty. One day I woke up and thought, 'Just go and sort it out! It will take about a day's work but once it's tidy, shiny and clean, you can be productive with your music and writing!' Sometimes, you just need to give yourself a good talking to – *self-discipline*!

If you feel your diet and habits of eating could be preventing you from being happy, radiant and full of energy, then take the *first step*. The first step is always the hardest, so don't put pressure on yourself. A couple of years ago I went through a phase of eating a lot – and I mean A LOT – of junk food. As a result, I put on about 30 pounds in weight, my hair became greasy, my skin suffered and even though I still socialized and managed to be happy, inwardly I was not as bright and cheerful as I could have been. Because of the huge amount of sugar I was consuming, I was having big sucrose highs then drastic lows. I complained silently to myself and even prayed fervently for help. Of course, God works in mysterious ways and He cannot help unless we put something into action. First, I stopped eating cakes, biscuits, sweets, crisps and fizzy drinks and joined a gym. However, even after attempting to do this for several weeks, I didn't lose any weight and still felt tired and lethargic. So I reassessed my diet. Yes, I had cut out all the obvious junk foods but was still managing to eat unhealthily. I somehow convinced myself that as long as I wasn't eating the more blatant offenders, such as the sweets and cakes, I could still eat whole pizzas and chips and cook everything in oil – every day!

Eventually I found a slimming class which enabled me to eat a lot of food but still lose weight. Then I looked again at my books on food combining – they make so much sense to my mind set and when I follow the principles I feel great and my mind clears, leaving me able to serve, be creative and not walk around all day feeling useless and tired. Principles in practice are far better than just kidding yourself into believing that you are improving your habits. You actually need to *action* the changes to make them work. As Eminem, a famous rap artist, so rightly says, 'You can do anything if you put your mind to it.'

Points to Consider

- Take the goals you want to achieve one day at a time.

- Love yourself along the way – at whatever point you happen to be at, feel happy that you are a creation of God and that you want to improve for the sake of being of service to yourself and humankind.

- Remember that while you may want to be an example for others, they can also be a good example to you. Be prepared to learn at any time and then integrate the good parts into your upgraded routine!

- Try not to beat yourself up about the wrong things you have done instead of forgiving and learning from mistakes – if you always focus on the bad you will come to a blocked wall at every turn and jeopardize any possibility of improving your general health.

  Turn unto Him, and fear not because of thy deeds. He, in truth, forgiveth whomsoever He desireth as a bounty on His part; no God is there but Him, the Ever-Forgiving, the All-Bounteous.

  Bahá'u'lláh[5]

- If you are not happy with your diet, make a trip to your local library or bookstore and search out something that will suit you and your lifestyle. There is no point following recipes that take hours to prepare and cook if you work full time.

- Write down a list of what you want to change in order to enjoy a happier, healthier life.

- Write down your goals and how you are going to set about achieving them.

- Do it today!

And now as I look into the future, I hope to see the friends at all times, in every land, and of every shade of thought and character, voluntarily and joyously rallying around their local and in particular their national centres of activity, upholding and promoting their interests with complete unanimity . . .

Shoghi Effendi[6]

Where Do I Go from Here?

First in a human being's way of life must be purity, then freshness, cleanliness, and independence of spirit.

'Abdu'l-Bahá[1]

If you want to obtain optimum health and well-being, you need to start thinking along the lines of working from the inside out. It is all very well placing a cloth over a dusty mirror to hide it from guests but cleaning it thoroughly will allow the mirror to shine and reflect the sun. You get my drift! It may be time for a complete spring clean of your body, which will have marvellous benefits and bounties for your entire self. I have friends who have been inspired through reading the Bahá'í writings to change their diets and general living habits. In making slight adjustments to their lives, they have been freed from numerous illnesses including depression and stress – both of which are worth not having – not to mention the amazingly positive health acquisitions they have enjoyed through their confident actions of self-progression.

Don't worry! You don't have to 'go it alone'. There are many ways to ensure that you feel empowered and enabled to make these positive steps. If you are already enjoying a healthy, happy life, perhaps your goal could be to stay that way and to encourage others to achieve the same, by giving inspirational talks, sharing not just your successes but your journeys and your pitfalls, or just by being a good support for friends and family while they go through changes and make life-altering decisions.

When I decided I would implement 'food combining' into my routine, you would be surprised at how many people were unsupportive of my decision. Some people hadn't heard of the books or the people connected to the principles so instantly dismissed the theories. Fear of the unknown is a great thing for some people, so if you are making new changes you may want either to organize an evening at which you can educate friends and family or just gradually let them know on a filtering basis. It can be quite difficult to introduce changes when others around you are content or *think* they are content as they are – people may feel inadequate, insecure or even envious that you are taking steps to alter your health and may feel judged for their 'bad health habits'. They don't realize that they too can do the same, as discussed, that they need to just take that one small step, which eventually will become giant leaps!

> Action inspired by confidence in the ultimate triumph of the Faith is, indeed, essential to the gradual and complete materialization of your hopes for the extension and consolidation of the Movement in your country. May the Almighty inspire each and every one of you with the zeal, determination, and faith to carry out His Will, and to proclaim His Message to those living in your land and beyond its confines.
>
> *Shoghi Effendi*[2]

Ideas

You may have your own plans and ideas about how you can start to improve your health but here are some for starters.

- Serve healthy food at feasts and firesides.

Apart from when I lived in Swaziland, where mainly fruit was served, I have rarely been to a Nineteen Day Feast that serves healthy foods. Of course, this doesn't bother me as I do like cakes and sweets now and then but what I wanted to do in our community was offer healthy foods *as well* so people could have more of a choice and a better awareness that all people have different eating habits. The first time my husband and I offered more healthy options was at a fireside about . . . health! We served carrot and celery sticks, hummus, crackers, nuts and raisins . . . it was a real success! We don't do it all the time but people favourably commented, saying how they liked the change and how good they felt afterwards.

- Be more supportive of fellow Bahá'ís' life choices.

If someone you know is taking steps for the sake of their health and you either don't agree with their programme or have no information on the type of diet or healthy step they are taking, consider investigating first. A Bahá'í friend of mine mentioned once to another Bahá'í that she was going on a health regime and she was publicly ridiculed! As a result, she came away from her friend feeling unsupported, dejected and miserable – and not so determined to go and improve her health. Support is crucial at times like these and words can alter your state of mind so much that you end up not following your goals.

- Be supportive of your children's individual health choices.

Of course, if you are cooking for four people, you don't want to prepare different meals for each one but if your child independently says that she wants to be a vegetarian, then perhaps you could study the writings together and allow your child to make that personal, informed choice. It is after all, 'approved' and 'more pleasing' than eating meat.

- Lead examples in communities, conventions and summer schools.

You don't have to be health conscious all the time – the point is, moderation in all things, respect for others' health habits and empowerment of oneself to be more of an example, especially if you are at events which people from all religions are attending. If, however, there is an opportunity to lead by example, even with something as seemingly insignificant as serving healthy food choices, then go ahead and seize it. You never know what conversations might start over a bowl of crudités!

- Help others to be healthy.

If friends or family want your support, they will generally ask for it. Be content with being a good example if they don't want 'one to one' interaction on health subjects. If they ask . . . well! Help them to plan and action their ideas. You could be their gym partner, their swimming buddy, their cycling friend or their walking companion. You could have evenings where you cook new and exciting but healthy dishes for one another and make scrapbooks of any ideas or recipes that promote good health. It is important, so don't shy away from it!

- Do not be afraid of change.

Allow yourself to make some changes without fear of being ridiculed. If you are the only vegetarian in your circle of friends, then so be it! Unity in diversity!

- Do things in moderation.

Whichever route you decide to take, bring the concept of moderation along with you to assist you on your journey. It is a great grounding tool and will ensure that you don't live life to excess, helping you to be healthier and happier.

- Choose forms of exercise that you enjoy.

It sounds too simple to be true but I know so many

people who put themselves through gruelling workouts and gym routines that they just don't enjoy. What's more, a lot of these people then start to make excuses not to go to the gym, so, effectively, they are just throwing away bags of money. A brisk walk, cycle ride, swimming and dancing lessons that appeal to your taste are great to keep you fit and in shape too. Make your choices and allow yourself to be flexible. Ideally, you should do some form of exercise that makes your heart race every day!

- Always have PMT.

That's right! **P**ositive **M**ental **T**hinking. It shapes the way you are as a person and helps you to deal with all the trials and stresses of life. It's there to assist you with health and diet changes and keeps you going when the going gets tough. There is the saying, 'It's no use crying over spilt milk as it may have been poisoned.' Having a more positive outlook will not only enable your body to be more relaxed and healthy but also your mind will reap the benefits and rewards that are awaiting you as soon as you implement those changes.

Take a good look at yourself, in and out of the mirror, and decide whether or not it is worth making any improvements. I personally feel that any alteration, however small, could initiate such a vast ripple effect that through one small action alone you could inspire thousands of people – and you won't even know it! To be concerned with your health is a good thing, a real positive acknowledgement of the fact that you are a creation of God. It is up to you now to lead the way and inspire others. I would love to hear any of your stories, ideas, recipes, suggestions and journeys to improving your health so please feel free to contact me at the address at the end of the book. I feel like I have been part of a very exciting workshop – one where I have learned just as much as I have written. Thank you for being a part of it too!

Be ye as a mountain in the Cause of your Lord, the Almighty, the All-Glorious, the Unconstrained.

Bahá'u'lláh[3]

13

Tablet to a Physician

This unauthorized translation of the Tablet by Bahá'u'lláh is published in Star of the West, vol. 13, no. 9, p. 252, December 1922.[1]

O God! The Supreme Knower! The Ancient Tongue speaks that which will satisfy the wise in the absence of doctors.

O People, do not eat except when you are hungry. Do not drink after you have retired to sleep.

Exercise is good when the stomach is empty; it strengthens the muscles. When the stomach is full it is very harmful.

Do not neglect medical treatment, when it is necessary, but leave it off when the body is in good condition.

Do not take nourishment except when (the process of) digestion is completed. Do not swallow until you have thoroughly masticated your food.

Treat disease first of all through diet, and refrain from medicine. If you can find what you need for healing in a single herb do not use a compound medicine. Leave off medicine when the health is good, and use it in case of necessity.

If two diametrically opposite foods are put on the

table do not mix them. Be content with one of them. Take first the liquid food before partaking of solid food. The taking of food before that which you have already eaten is digested is dangerous . . .

When you have eaten walk a little that the food may settle.

That which is difficult to masticate is forbidden by the wise. Thus the Supreme Pen commands you.

A light meal in the morning is as a light to the body.

Avoid all harmful habits; they cause unhappiness in the world.

Search for the causes of diseases. This saying is the conclusion of this utterance.

14

A Few Recipes

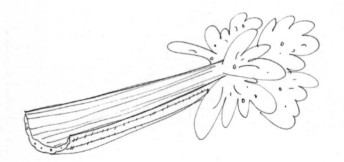

In all circumstances they should conduct themselves with moderation; if the meal be only one
course this is more pleasing in the sight of God;
however, according to their means, they should
seek to have this single dish be of good quality.

Bahá'u'lláh[1]

There isn't just one single route to 'health' that each and
every one of us can happily follow – everyone is different and has varied tastes and choices when it comes
to leading a healthy life. Some people swear by being a
vegetarian while others enjoy the benefits of eating meat
and still remain fit and active. Some enjoy going to the
gym to work out while others enjoy cycling and walking.
You have to find what suits you. I know that there will be
a variety of people reading this book who will also have
differing tastes in food so what I shall do is simply share
recipes that I have experienced or concocted through
trial and error and you can feel free to experiment with
your own dishes or change the ones in this book. I am
a busy person so my meals are often nutritious and easy
to prepare as well as being simple yet filling! Also, as I
food combine almost one hundred per cent these days,
my meal ideas are striving to be well-combined meals.
If you eat meat, then the general idea is that you don't
combine it with any starch foods. So you could have
chicken or fish with lovely big salads instead! Have one
concentrated food then make up the rest of your meal
with salad and vegetables. For more recipes and ideas,

check out the recommended reading list at the back of the book. All recipes serve four people. Measurements given are metric and Imperial – use only one set.

Soups, Salads and Sandwiches

Lentil and Lime Soup

This is one of my favourite dishes and it is so filling, so low fat and so delicious!

You will need:
250 g/8 oz red split or puy lentils
3 limes
1 lemon
2 sticks celery
2 carrots
1 large onion
1 clove garlic
vegetable bouillon (10 g per half litre/2 teaspoons per pint of water)
1 litre/2 pints of water
salt and pepper

Method:
- Wash the celery and carrots and chop into small bite size pieces.
- Roughly chop the onion and garlic.
- Heat a large saucepan and fry the onions and garlic in a little olive oil (or alternatively, some water, which is

known as dry frying) for about three to five minutes on a medium heat.
- Add the stock, celery, carrot and lentils.
- Bring to the boil and then simmer for approximately 20 minutes.
- Add the juice of 1 lime and 1 lemon. Stir in and simmer for a further 5 minutes.
- Serve with black pepper and half a lime per bowl.

Barley Soup

You will need:
1 litre/2 pints water
112 g/4 oz pot or pearl barley
112 g/4 oz red lentils
4 large potatoes, cut into chunks
2 leeks or 1 onion, chopped
1 or 2 carrots, sliced
1 stick celery, chopped
handful of parsley, chopped
few sprigs of thyme (or a little dried thyme) (optional)
salt and pepper
little cream or milk (optional)

Method:
- Put water into a large pot and bring to the boil.
- Add barley and red lentils and bring back to the boil.
- Turn down heat and simmer until the barley is tender, about an hour.

- Add potatoes, vegetables and herbs, reserving a little chopped parsley for garnish.
- Cook for another half hour or until potatoes are soft. You may need to add more water.
- Season with salt and pepper.
- When ready to serve, remove from heat and add cream or milk to pot.
- Garnish with chopped parsley.

Portuguese Soupa

You will need:
500 g/1 lb potatoes, peeled and chopped
500 ml/1 pint water
1 carrot, grated
two or three cabbage leaves, shredded
salt

Method:
- Put chopped potatoes into cold water in a large pot and bring to the boil.
- Turn down the heat and simmer until the potatoes are very soft.
- Use a hand blender to puree the potatoes gently until thick or a fork to mash them thoroughly. You may need to add water to make a soup-like consistency.
- Add grated carrot and shredded cabbage to the soup and stir.
- Add salt to taste.
- Cook until cabbage is limp and the soup is thick.

Salad with Chickpeas

You will need:
2 cans of chickpeas (in water)
4 carrots
12 radishes
4 spring onions
lettuce of any variety
cherry tomatoes

Method:
- Wash and prepare all the salad items to your taste.
- Drain the chickpeas.
- Combine together in a bowl.
- Serve with lemon/pickle/salt and pepper.

Salad with Sweet Potato*

You will need:
salad ingredients as above
4 sweet potatoes
lemon juice
olive oil

Method:
- Prepare the salad as before (with or without chickpeas).
- Preheat the oven to 180 C/ 350 F.
- Wash the sweet potatoes thoroughly and pierce with a fork.

- Brush over lightly with lemon/olive oil.
- Cook for approximately 45 minutes (depending on size).
- Serve with salad.

* For an alternative, cook baby potatoes for 30 minutes at 180 C/350 F and serve with salad with hummus if desired.

Fruity Feta Cheese and Romano Pepper Salad

You will need:
2 Romano peppers
168 g/6 oz feta cheese (if you don't like feta, then any cheese to your taste will suffice!)
4 spring onions
4 sticks celery
4 carrots
8 radishes
4 ripe nectarines
lettuce of any variety
pickle (optional)

Method:
- De-seed the pepper, cut down the middle and slice thinly.
- Cut the cheese into cubes.
- Peel the outer skin off the spring onions and slice lengthways, thinly.
- Chop the celery, carrots and radish into small pieces.

- Slice the nectarines in half, take out the stones and slice into bite-size pieces.
- Prepare the lettuce in thin strips.
- Mix all the above together and serve alone or with a teaspoon of pickle.

Tabbouleh

You will need:
250 g/8 oz cracked wheat (burghul wheat)
1 onion or a few spring onions, chopped fine
2–3 large bunches parsley
handful of fresh mint
4 large tomatoes, chopped
juice of 3 lemons
salt to taste
2 tablespoons olive oil (optional)

Method:
- Soak cracked wheat in water overnight or for at least a few hours.
- When soft, drain thoroughly, pressing the water out completely.
- Chop parsley and mint finely or whizz in a food processor.
- Add parsley and mint to drained wheat and mix thoroughly.
- De-seed tomatoes, then chop finely and drain.
- Add tomatoes to tabbouleh.
- If using oil, stir into tabbouleh thoroughly.

- Stir in lemon juice.
- Add salt to taste.

Avocado on Granary Toast

You will need:
2 large avocados (they are ripe when they yield to pressure)
juice of 2 lemons
4 mushrooms, sliced thinly
8 cherry tomatoes, sliced thinly
8 slices granary bread (use any wholemeal/gluten-free alternative)
rocket lettuce or other salad garnish
black pepper

Method:
- Mash the avocados with a fork in a good-sized bowl.
- Squeeze in the lemon juice and grind in the black pepper.
- Toast lightly one side of the bread under a medium grill.
- Spread the avocado mixture generously on the untoasted side of the bread.
- Place on the tomatoes and mushrooms.
- Toast for about a minute under the grill.
- Serve with rocket lettuce or any salad garnish.

Hummus Pitta Pockets

You will need:
8 pitta pockets
200 g/8 oz tub hummus
2 big handfuls lettuce of your choice
2 big handfuls baby spinach leaves
8 baby vine ripened tomatoes
2 sprigs parsley
2 tablespoons olive oil
juice of 1 lemon

Method:
- Chop all the salad items finely and mix in a bowl with the olive oil and lemon juice.
- Sprinkle water onto the pitta pockets and heat under a medium warm grill for two minutes.
- Split the pitta pockets.
- Spread hummus onto the inside of the pockets.
- Stuff the salad into the pockets and serve.

Chickpea Sandwiches

You will need:
456 g/16 oz canned chickpeas, drained
1–2 cloves garlic, peeled
juice of 1 lemon
handful of parsley, roughly chopped
3–4 tablespoons very low fat natural fromage frais
salt and pepper

8 slices wholemeal bread, toasted

Method:
- Roughly blend chickpeas with garlic in a food processor or mash thoroughly with a fork.
- Add lemon juice.
- Stir in parsley and fromage frais.
- Season to taste.
- Spread on toast.

Main Meals

Roasted Vegetables with Garlic and Lemon

You will need:
4 courgettes, cut lengthways
4 red peppers, de-seeded and cut into chunks
2 red-skinned onions, quartered
4 carrots, cut into large pieces
4 parsnips, cut lengthways
500 g/1 lb new or baby potatoes, halved
2 cloves garlic, peeled
2 tablespoons extra virgin olive oil
juice of 1 lemon
black pepper

Method:
- Preheat the oven to 180 C/350 F.
- Place vegetables on a large baking tray or in a large dish.
- Mix olive oil, lemon juice and black pepper together and drizzle over the vegetables.
- Cook in the heated oven for approximately 30 to 40 minutes.
- Serve the roasted vegetables with onion gravy or simply on their own!

Eating the garlic is optional but simply placing it next to the other vegetables will add an extra dimension to the tastes!

Roasted Butternut Squash and Haloumi Cheese

You will need:
2 medium or large butternut squashes
3 tablespoons olive oil
juice of 1 lemon
black pepper
224 g/ 8 oz haloumi cheese, sliced

Method:
- Preheat oven to 220 C/450 F.
- Top and tail butternut squash and cut in half lengthways.
- Remove seeds with a spoon.
- Score the flesh lengthways and across, making cube

shapes (taking care not to cut right through to the other side).

- Squeeze the lemon juice over each half, pour on the olive oil and grind the black pepper.
- Put the butternut squash halves in the oven for 30 to 40 minutes or until they test soft with a fork.
- Remove from oven.
- Place slices of haloumi cheese over the butternut squash halves.
- Return to oven briefly to melt cheese.
- Serve with a garden salad.

Linguine with Rocket

You will need:
350 g/12 oz linguine pasta per person
2 large handfuls of rocket lettuce, shredded
2 cloves of garlic
juice of 1 lime
500 g/1 lb cherry or vine ripened tomatoes
2 teaspoons sweet chilli sauce
black pepper

Method:
- Cook linguine to al dente in plenty of boiling water, salted if you wish.
- Peel the tomatoes (slice a cross at the top of each and place in a bowl of boiling water, then slip off skins).
- Chop peeled tomatoes.
- Crush the garlic with a little salt or in a garlic press.

- Drain linguine when cooked. Toss the tomatoes, garlic, shredded rocket, lime juice, black pepper and sweet chilli sauce into the hot linguine and serve.

Spaghetti with Avocado

You will need:
500 g/1 lb spaghetti
2 large ripe avocados, chopped
224 g/8 oz cherry tomatoes, cut in half
big handful fresh basil, broken
2 garlic cloves, sliced
1 tsp olive oil
juice of 1 lemon
salt

Method:
- Cook spaghetti to al dente in plenty of boiling water, salted if you wish.
- Heat oil in a pan.
- Fry garlic gently until golden.
- Turn off heat.
- Add tomatoes and avocado to the pan and stir gently (do not cook them).
- Add basil and lemon juice and a little salt.
- Drain spaghetti when cooked. Toss the tomatoes and avocado into the hot spaghetti and serve.

Basmati Rice with Oven-Baked Vegetables

You will need:
500 g/1 lb brown basmati rice (this is about 3 cups)
4 carrots, peeled and cut lengthways
2 red peppers, de-seeded and sliced into two
6 shallot onions
4 courgettes
1 clove garlic, cut in half
1 tablespoon olive oil
juice of 1 lemon
2 avocados, sliced
hummus

Method:
- Preheat oven to 180 C/350 F.
- Mix olive oil and lemon juice.
- Put vegetables into a large dish and drizzle over the olive oil and lemon juice.
- Bake vegetables for approximately 30 minutes until tender.
- Cook the rice according to the directions on the packet.

OR

- Measure the rice in teacups. For each teacup of rice, put one teacup of water into a large pan plus one extra teacup of water. So for 3 teacups of rice, put 4 teacups of water into a pan.

- Boil the water.
- When the water is boiling, add the rice and bring back to the boil briefly.
- Turn down the heat to low and simmer for 25 to 40 minutes or until all the water is absorbed and the rice is tender and fluffy. Watch carefully and add a little more water if required.
- When the vegetables are cooked, cut into small pieces and mix with the rice.
- Serve with avocado and hummus.

Easy Chilli

You will need:
3 tins kidney beans, drained
2 tins chopped tomatoes
3 sticks celery, chopped
1 medium onion, chopped
1 small green, red or yellow pepper, chopped
1 tablespoon hot chilli powder (or more, to taste)
salt to taste
56 g/2 oz cracked wheat
cheddar cheese, grated (optional)

Method:
- Put all ingredients except cracked wheat and cheese into a large pan and bring to the boil.
- Add cracked wheat.
- Turn down to simmer.
- Cook until cracked wheat is tender, about 30 minutes.

You can serve at this point but it is better if it stands for a while before eating.
- Top with a little grated cheese if desired.

Vegetarian Shepherd's Pie

You will need:
168 g/6 oz green or brown lentils
112 g/4 oz yellow split peas
1 medium onion, chopped
½ green pepper, chopped
2 carrots, sliced
2 sticks celery, chopped
1 clove garlic, crushed
2 pinches ground nutmeg
dash or two cayenne pepper
salt to taste
Topping:
500 g/1 lb potatoes, cooked and mashed
250 g/½ lb tomatoes, sliced
56 g/2 oz cheddar cheese, grated (optional)

Method:
- Boil water in a large pan.
- Add lentils and peas to boiling water and rapidly boil for about 10 minutes.
- Turn down heat and simmer until tender (not mushy), about half an hour.
- Add chopped vegetables to legumes and cook a further 5 minutes.

- Drain, reserving water for another use (e.g. soup) if required.
- Season with salt, nutmeg and cayenne pepper.
- Put into deep, ovenproof dish.
- Top with sliced tomatoes, sprinkle with a little salt.
- Pile mashed potatoes over the tomatoes.
- Sprinkle with cheese if desired.
- Bake at 250 C/475 F until top is brown and the pie is bubbling.

Vegetable Stew*

You will need:
2 medium onions
3 garlic cloves
1 aubergine
2 courgettes
3 sticks celery
2 parsnips
2 carrots
1 red pepper
1 green pepper
170 g/6 oz spinach
2 bay leaves
4 tablespoons olive oil
250 ml/½ pint water
400 g/14 oz tin tomatoes
¼ teaspoon chili powder
½ teaspoon dried thyme
½ teaspoon dried oregano

1 tablespoon pesto or fresh basil leaves
salt and pepper

Method:
- Cut the onions, aubergine, courgettes, celery, parsnips, carrots, spinach and peppers into bite-size pieces and place in saucepan.
- Crush the garlic and add to pan.
- Add all other ingredients apart from pesto and salt and pepper.
- Bring to the boil and cook for 25 to 30 minutes until all vegetables are tender.
- Stir in pesto or basil, season to taste and serve.

* You can also make this into a delicious soup.
- Proceed as above.
- Put in liquidizer and blend until smooth.
- Return to a saucepan and stir in the same volume of water.
- Heat and serve.

Feast Foods

Verily, it is enjoined upon you to offer a feast, once in every month, though only water be served; for God hath purposed to bind hearts together, albeit through both earthly and heavenly means.

Bahá'u'lláh[2]

The Nineteen Day Feast is a spiritual, administrative and social occasion for the whole Baháʼí community. Hosts of the Nineteen Day Feast often serve a variety of simple refreshments. Let the physical food match the spiritual food and occasionally offer something a little more healthy than the usual cakes and biscuits. Each recipe serves at least 8–10 people with other foods.

Chickpea Snack

You will need:

4 tins chickpeas, drained
1 tablespoon olive oil
cayenne pepper to taste (about 1 teaspoon if you like them spicy!)
salt to taste

Method:
- Line 2 baking sheets with aluminium foil.
- Preheat oven to 200 C/ 400 F.
- Place drained chickpeas in a large bowl.
- Add olive oil and stir thoroughly.
- Add cayenne pepper and salt to taste, stirring until the chickpeas are coated.
- Turn the peas onto the baking sheets and spread into a single layer.
- Toast in the oven for about an hour to an hour and a half, stirring occasionally, until the chickpeas are dry, golden and crunchy. Check them often, as

towards the end they will suddenly begin to burn unless watched carefully.

- When cool, store in an airtight container.

Crudités and California Dip

You will need:
a selection of vegetables (try celery, carrots, peppers, cucumbers, turnips, broccoli, cauliflower, baby sweetcorn, spring onions, cherry tomatoes, snow peas, baby button mushrooms)

For the dip:
200 g/8 oz tub cream cheese (you can use the low-fat type if you wish)
approximately 50 g/2 oz plain yogurt
½ packet French onion soup mix

Method:
Make the dip several hours before you want to use it.

- Turn cream cheese into a bowl and soften by stirring.
- Add yogurt a little at a time. Mixture should be thick.
- Stir in the dry onion soup mix.
- Cover and refrigerate until ready to serve. (The onion soup mix will soften with time.)
- Wash and peel vegetables as appropriate.
- Cut celery, carrots, peppers, cucumbers and turnips into large strips.

- Break broccoli and cauliflower into florets.
- Leave baby sweetcorn, spring onions, cherry tomatoes, snow peas and baby button mushrooms whole.
- Arrange vegetables in an attractive design on a large platter or in a big basket and serve with dip.

Guacamole

You will need:
2 large very ripe avocados
1 tablespoon plain yogurt
juice of 1 lemon
1 teaspoon chilli powder (more, if you like it spicy)
pinch of garlic powder
salt to taste
1 tomato, chopped and drained (optional)
tortilla chips, crackers or crudités

Method:
- Peel and mash the avocados.
- Mix in yogurt, lemon juice, chilli powder, garlic and salt.
- Cover and refrigerate until ready to serve.
- Just before you serve, stir in tomatoes.
- Serve with tortilla chips, crackers or crudités (prepared as above).

Stuffed Celery

You will need:

2 heads of celery (choose celery with deep grooves, if possible)

200 g/ 8 oz tub cream cheese (you can use the low-fat type if you wish)*

1 teaspoon poppy seeds OR toasted sesame seeds

Method:

- Separate the celery into stalks, wash thoroughly and pat dry.
- Remove leaves (save a few for decoration) and root end from each stalk.
- Cut the celery stalks into sticks about 80 mm/3 inches long.
- Mix cream cheese with poppy seeds or sesame seeds.
- Using a small spoon, fill the groove of each celery stick.
- Arrange attractively on a large platter or tray and decorate with celery leaves.

*You can also use California dip, hummus or plain cream cheese for this recipe.

Fresh Fruit Platter

You will need:
a selection of fresh fruit (in spring and summer try nectarines, peaches, oranges, melon, bananas, plums, figs, mango, papaya, pineapple, grapes, strawberries, raspberries, blueberries; in autumn and winter try apples, pears, tangerines, pineapple, bananas, grapes)
juice of 1 lemon
a few fresh mint leaves

Method:
- Wash and prepare fruit as appropriate.
- Cut nectarines, peaches, apples and pears into eighths.
- Cut oranges and tangerines into sections, slices or quarters.
- Cut melon into slices or large chunks.
- Peel bananas and cut into large chunks.
- Cut plums and figs into quarters or leave them whole.
- Cut mango, papaya and pineapple into slices.
- Leave grapes, strawberries, raspberries and blueberries whole.
- Arrange fruit on a large platter.
- Sprinkle with lemon juice.
- Decorate with mint leaves and serve.

Dried Fruit and Nut Platter*

You will need:
a selection of dried fruit (try dates, figs, apricots, peaches, apples, prunes, raisins, sultanas)
a selection of nuts (try walnuts, pecans, Brazil nuts, hazelnuts, almonds and pistachios)
cream cheese (optional)
tangerines

Method:
- If using cream cheese, remove pits from dates and stuff with cream cheese.
- Remove shells from nuts (leave shells on pistachios).
- Arrange fruit and nuts in an attractive pattern on a large platter and serve with a basket of tangerines.

*Be careful when using nuts, as some people are allergic to them.

15

Good Health Matters

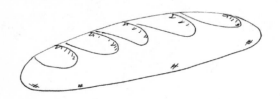

There are so many Bahá'í writings that I have found on the matter of health that I could not possibly discuss them all in this book, so this final chapter is a compilation of inspiring, thought-provoking and mind-easing quotations which, I hope, will provide you with tools and references for your future investigation. I have enjoyed the whole experience of writing, researching and exploring the issues discussed in this book, which has taught me so much! Yet there is always more knowledge one can acquire so use the following quotations to assist you in your quest for better health and increased spiritual capacity! ENJOY!

It is more kingly to be satisfied with a crust of stale bread than to enjoy a sumptuous dinner of many courses, the money for which comes out of the pockets of others. The mind of a contented person is always peaceful and his heart at rest.

'Abdu'l-Bahá[1]

Turning the face towards God brings healing to the body, the mind and the soul.

'Abdu'l-Bahá[2]

Be ye the very essence of cleanliness amongst mankind. This, truly, is what your Lord, the Incomparable, the All-Wise, desireth for you.

Bahá'u'lláh[3]

Adopt ye such usages as are most in keeping with refinement. He, verily, desireth to see in you the manners of the inmates of Paradise in His mighty and most sublime Kingdom. Hold ye fast unto refinement under all conditions, that your eyes may be preserved from beholding what is repugnant both to your own selves and to the dwellers of Paradise.

Bahá'u'lláh[4]

Cleave ye unto the cord of refinement with such tenacity as to allow no trace of dirt to be seen upon your garments. Such is the injunction of One Who is sanctified above all refinement.

Bahá'u'lláh[5]

Immerse yourselves in clean water; it is not permissible to bathe yourselves in water that hath already been used.

Bahá'u'lláh[6]

Truly, We desire to behold you as manifestations of paradise on earth, that there may be diffused from you such fragrance as shall rejoice the hearts of the favoured of God.

Bahá'u'lláh[7]

All that has been created is for man, who is at the apex of creation, and he must be thankful for the divine bestowals. All material things are for us, so

that through our gratitude we may learn to understand life as a divine benefit. If we are disgusted with
life we are ingrates, for our material and spiritual
existence are the outward evidences of the divine
mercy. Therefore we must be happy and spend our
time in praises, appreciating all things.

'Abdu'l-Bahá[8]

If the health and well-being of the body be expended
in the path of the Kingdom, this is very acceptable
and praiseworthy; and if it is expended to the benefit
of the human world in general – even though it be
to their material benefit and be a means of doing
good – that is also acceptable. But if the health and
welfare of man be spent in sensual desires, in a life
on the animal plane, and in devilish pursuits – then
disease is better than such health; nay, death itself
is preferable to such a life. If thou art desirous of
health, wish thou health for serving the Kingdom. I
hope thou mayest attain a perfect insight, an inflex-
ible resolution, a complete health and spiritual and
physical strength in order that thou mayest drink
from the fountain of eternal life and be assisted by
the spirit of divine confirmation.

'Abdu'l-Bahá[9]

All true healing comes from God! There are two
causes for sickness, one is material, the other spiritual. If the sickness is of the body, a material remedy
is needed, if of the soul, a spiritual remedy.

If the heavenly benediction be upon us while we are being healed then only can we be made whole, for medicine is but the outward and visible means through which we obtain the heavenly healing. Unless the spirit be healed, the cure of the body is worth nothing. All is in the hands of God, and without Him there can be no health in us!

There have been many men who have died at last of the very disease of which they have made a special study. Aristotle, for instance, who made a special study of the digestion, died of a gastronomic malady. Aviseu was a specialist of the heart, but he died of heart disease. God is the great compassionate Physician who alone has the power to give true healing.

'Abdu'l-Bahá[10]

This is worship: to serve mankind and to minister to the needs of the people. Service is prayer. A physician ministering to the sick, gently, tenderly, free from prejudice and believing in the solidarity of the human race, he is giving praise.

'Abdu'l-Bahá[11]

The healing that is by the power of the Holy Spirit needs no special concentration or contact. It is through the wish or desire and the prayer of the holy person. The one who is sick may be in the East and the healer in the West, and they may not have been acquainted with each other, but as soon as that holy person turns his heart to God and begins to pray, the sick one is healed. This is a gift belonging to the Holy Manifestations and those who are in the highest station.

'Abdu'l-Bahá[12]

Bibliography

'Abdu'l-Bahá. *Paris Talks*. London: Bahá'í Publishing Trust, 1967.
— *The Promulgation of Universal Peace*. Wilmette, IL: Bahá'í Publishing Trust, 1982.
— *Selections from the Writings of 'Abdu'l-Bahá*. Haifa: Bahá'í World Centre, 1978.
— *Some Answered Questions*. Wilmette, IL: Bahá'í Publishing Trust, 1981.
Bahá'í World Faith. Wilmette, IL: Bahá'í Publishing Trust, 2nd edn. 1976.
Bahá'u'lláh. *Epistle to the Son of the Wolf*. Wilmette, IL: Bahá'í Publishing Trust, 1988.
— *Gleanings from the Writings of Bahá'u'lláh*. Wilmette, IL: Bahá'í Publishing Trust, 1983.
— *The Hidden Words*. Wilmette, IL: Bahá'í Publishing Trust, 1990.
— *The Kitáb-i-Aqdas*. Haifa: Bahá'í World Centre, 1992.
— *Tablets of Bahá'u'lláh*. Wilmette, IL: Bahá'í Publishing Trust, 1988.
BBC News Home Page – Internet – http://news.bbc.co.uk/1/hi/health/774434.stm
The Compilation of Compilations. Prepared by the Universal House of Justice 1963–1990. 2 vols. [Mona Vale NSW]: Bahá'í Publications Australia, 1991.
Esslemont, J. E. *Bahá'u'lláh and the New Era*. London: Bahá'í

Publishing Trust, 1974.

Grundy, Julia M. *Ten Days in the Light of 'Akká*. Wilmette, IL: Bahá'í Publishing Trust, 1979.

Lights of Guidance: A Bahá'í Reference File. Compiled by Helen Hornby. New Delhi: Bahá'í Publishing Trust, 2nd edn. 1988.

Promoting Entry by Troops: A Statement and Compilation Prepared by the Research Department of the Universal House of Justice. Mona Vale NSW: Bahá'í Publications Australia, 1994.

Shoghi Effendi. *The Advent of Divine Justice*. Wilmette, IL: Bahá'í Publishing Trust, 1990.

— *Bahá'í Administration*. Wilmette, IL: Bahá'í Publishing Trust, 1968.

Star of the West. rpt. Oxford: George Ronald, 1984.

www.bahai-library.org

The author can be contacted through George Ronald Publisher Ltd. at sales@grbooks.com

Suggested Reading

Diamond, Harvey and Marilyn Diamond. *Fit For Life*. New York: Warner Books, 1986.

This book explores the history behind the science of food combining and provides a four-week eating plan and information on the digestive system.

Fuhrman, Joel. *Eat To Live*. London: Piatkus, 2003.

Dr Fuhrman suggests how we can start eating to live and not living to eat. He guides us through eating plans not just for weight loss but also to remedy a whole host of illnesses and diseases that are common in today's world.

Habgood, Jackie. *The Hay Diet Made Easy: A Practical Guide to Food Combining*. London: Souvenir Press, 1997.

This book is full of menu ideas and advice for people who want to introduce the principles of the Hay Diet into their routine. Very easy to follow and a great starting place for food combiners.

Vale, Jason. *Slim 4 Life: Freedom From the Food Trap*. London: HarperCollins, 2002.

> A great read for people who want to completely reassess their eating habits and be educated about how to gain a healthy, trim body and freedom from the foods that make us ill.

www.closertothedream.com

> Brought to people across the globe, courtesy of the company Closer to the Dream, this website features an exciting, free online magazine, which aims to inspire, inform and promote a healthy lifestyle, mind, body and soul. It is a great tool for taking those steps towards better health. This is also the website where you can subscribe to the monthly DVD magazine *Inspiring Heart*, which aims to inspire and encourage people to achieve more in their lives and to share with them through innovative and informative interviews and articles the positive and uplifting things that are going on in the world.

References and Notes

Introduction
1. Attributed to 'Abdu'l-Bahá, in Grundy, *Ten Days in the Light of 'Akká*, pp. 8–9.
2. Bahá'u'lláh, *Tablets*, p. 138.

Chapter 1
1. From a letter written on behalf of Shoghi Effendi to an individual, 17 July 1937, in *Lights of Guidance*, pp. 291–2, no. 991.
2. Bahá'u'lláh, *Hidden Words*, Persian no. 5.
3. Bahá'u'lláh, *Gleanings*, p. 305.
4. From a letter written on behalf of Shoghi Effendi to an individual, 17 July 1937, in *Lights of Guidance*, pp. 291–2, no. 991.
5. 'Abdu'l-Bahá, *Promulgation*, p. 453.
6. 'Abdu'l-Bahá, *Selections*, p. 34.

Chapter 2
1. From a letter written on behalf of Shoghi Effendi to an individual, 17 July 1937, in *Lights of Guidance*, p. 292, no. 991.
2. Bahá'u'lláh, *Gleanings*, p. 149.
3. 'Abdu'l-Bahá, *Promulgation*, p. 204.
4. From a letter written on behalf of Shoghi Effendi to an individual, 23 November 1947.
5. 'Abdu'l-Bahá, in *Bahá'í World Faith*, p. 375.

Chapter 3
1. From a letter written on behalf of Shoghi Effendi to two individuals, 15 September 1952, in *Lights of Guidance*, p. 291, no. 990.

2. Bahá'u'lláh, *Gleanings*, p. 288.
3. Bahá'u'lláh, in *Star of the West*, vol. 13, no. 9, p. 252. This translation is unauthorized.
4. 'Abdu'l-Bahá, *Bahá'í World Faith*, p. 384.
5. Bahá'u'lláh, in *Star of the West*, vol. 13, no. 9, p. 252. This translation is unauthorized.
6. Bahá'u'lláh, *Tablets*, p. 138.

Chapter 4
1. 'Abdu'l-Bahá, *Selections, p. 152.*
2. 'Abdu'l-Bahá, *Some Answered Questions*, p. 257.

Chapter 5
1. *'Abdu'l-Bahá, Selections, p. 152.*
2. 'Abdu'l-Bahá, in *Star of the West*, vol. 8, no. 18, pp. 229–30.

Chapter 6
1. From a Tablet of 'Abdu'l-Bahá to an individual, in *Lights of Guidance,* p. 294, no. 1005.
2. BBC News Home Page – Internet – http://news.bbc.co.uk/1/hi/health/774434.stm
3. 'Abdu'l-Bahá, *Selections*, p. 151.

Chapter 7
1. Attributed to 'Abdu'l-Bahá, in Grundy, *Ten Days in the Light of 'Akká,* pp. 8–9.
2. Bahá'u'lláh, *Epistle to the Son of the Wolf*, p. 47.

Chapter 8
1. From a Tablet of 'Abdu'l-Bahá to an individual, in *Lights of Guidance,* p. 295, no. 1006.
2. ibid.
3. ibid.
4. From a Tablet of 'Abdu'l-Bahá to an individual, in ibid. p. 295, no. 1007.
5. From a letter written on behalf of the Universal House of

Justice to an individual, 24 January 1977.

6. From a letter written on behalf of Shoghi Effendi to an individual, 9 July 1931, in *Lights of Guidance*, p. 296, no. 1010.

Chapter 9

1. 'Abdu'l-Bahá, *Selections, pp. 153–4*.
2. ibid. p. 156.
3. 'Abdu'l-Bahá, *Some Answered Questions*, pp. 258–9.
4. 'Abdu'l-Bahá, *Selections*, p. 153.

Chapter 10

1. 'Abdu'l-Bahá, *Selections, p. 150*.
2. Bahá'u'lláh, *Kitáb-i-Aqdas*, para. 119.
3. 'Abdu'l-Bahá, *Selections*, pp. 147–8.
4. From a letter of the Universal House of Justice to a National Spiritual Assembly, 15 April 1965, in *Lights of Guidance*, p. 353, no. 1183.
5. 'Abdu'l-Bahá, *Selections*, p. 150.

Chapter 11

1. From a letter written on behalf of Shoghi Effendi to an individual, in *Promoting Entry by Troops*, p. 26, no. 10.
2. From a letter written on behalf of Shoghi Effendi to an individual, 19 October 1947.
3. 'Abdu'l-Bahá, *Selections*, p. 147.
4. 'Abdu'l-Bahá, quoted in Bahá'u'lláh, *Kitáb-i-Aqdas*, note 104, p. 212.
5. Bahá'u'lláh, *Kitáb-i-Aqdas*, para. 184.
6. Shoghi Effendi, *Bahá'í Administration*, p. 67.

Chapter 12

1. *'Abdu'l-Bahá, Selections, p. 146*.
2. From a letter written on behalf of Shoghi Effendi to an individual, *Promoting Entry by Troops*, pp. 24–5.
3. Bahá'u'lláh, in Shoghi Effendi, *Advent of Divine Justice*, p. 82.

Chapter 13

1. A provisional translation of the whole Tablet by Khazeh Fananapazir, as well as information about it by the Universal House of Justice, can be found on www.bahai-library.org

Chapter 14

1. Bahá'u'lláh, in *Compilation,* vol. 1, p. 459, no. 1016.
2. Bahá'u'lláh, *Kitáb-i-Aqdas,* para. 57.

Chapter 15

1. 'Abdu'l-Bahá, in Esslemont, *Bahá'u'lláh and the New Era,* p. 98.
2. ibid. p. 97.
3. Bahá'u'lláh, *Kitáb-i-Aqdas,* para. 74.
4. ibid. para. 46.
5. ibid. para. 74.
6. ibid. para. 106.
7. ibid.
8. 'Abdu'l-Bahá, in Esslemont, *Bahá'u'lláh and the New Era,* p. 99.
9. 'Abdu'l-Bahá, in *Bahá'í World Faith,* p. 376.
10. 'Abdu'l-Bahá, *Paris Talks,* p. 19.
11. ibid. p. 177.
12. 'Abdu'l-Bahá, in *Compilation,* vol. 1, p. 475, no. 1051.